A Curious Street

The Ikon Maker
The Diamonds at the Bottom of the Sea
and other stories
The Leaves on Grey
Children of Lir:
Stories from Ireland

A Curious Street

by

DESMOND HOGAN

George Braziller

NEW YORK

Published in the United States in 1984 by George Braziller, Inc.

First published in England by Hamish Hamilton, Ltd, London, 1984.
Copyright © 1984 by Desmond Hogan
Parts of this novel have appeared in *Iowa Review*, the *Fiction
Magazine*, *The Anthology* (Irish Writers' Co-operative) and *Firebird 3:
Writing Today*, ed. Robin Robertson, Penguin Books Ltd.

Library of Congress Cataloging in Publication Data
Hogan, Desmond.
    A curious street.
    I. Title.
PR6058.0346C8   1984   823'.914   84-9382
ISBN 0-8076-1099-2

Printed in the United States of America
FIRST EDITION

In memory of Pat Murphy

Acknowledgements

I am grateful for permission to quote the verse from 'Exodus to Connacht', translated from the Irish by Thomas Kinsella from *An Duanaire 1600–1900: Poems of the Dispossessed*, The Dolmen Press, 1981. The verse from 'Grief of a Girl's heart' translated from the Irish by Lady Augusta Gregory is from *Kiltartan Poetry Book*, 1919.

The lines from 'Ferry 'cross the Mersey' (Gerrard Marsden) © 1964 are reproduced by kind permission of Dick James Music Ltd., London. The lines from 'Good Vibrations (Brian Wilson/Mike Love) © 1966 by Irving Music Inc., reproduced by permission of Rondor Music (London) Ltd. The lines from 'I'm a Believer' by Neil Diamond © 1966 by Screen Gems-Emi Music Inc., 6920 Sunset Blvd., Hollywood, California. Used by permission. All rights reserved. Also by permission of Screen Gems-Emi Music Ltd., London. The lines from 'A Young Girl' (English lyric of 'Une Enfant') – English lyric by Oscar Brown Jnr. Music by Charles Aznavour. Used by permission of Westminster Music Ltd.

Intreat me not to leave thee, or to return from following after thee: for whither thou goest, I will go; and where thou lodgest, I will lodge: thy people shall be my people, and thy God my God.

Ruth

Prologue

2 September 1977. I go into a newsagent's on the Falls Road, Belfast. I pick up a Southern Irish newspaper. In a paragraph on the bottom left hand side of the front page I see that Alan Mulvanney, a bachelor, has been found shot in the head beside the Shannon in Athlone. No foul play is suspected. I do not see Alan as he must have been at the time of his death but as the Alan my mother knew, black haired, pale skinned, red lipped, his black head among the early autumn poppies and a hand with an onyx ring on one of the fingers reaching onto the bank of the river.

Childhood

[1]

Alan Mulvanney was born on 10 December 1919. He grew up in a town full of fogs, of men slithering along in long overcoats, of little boys in sleeveless white jerseys. A red faced and authoritative aunt, observing him at an early age, called him 'a changeling'. He'd been left by the fairies in place of the child born to his mother. True he had a surprising shock of Spanish black curls, a pale face and lips always tentative, always about to ask a question. He slinked about Athlone by himself in a little blue coat, a belt at the back, hands behind his back. He asked questions of men painting shop-fronts, and of road sweepers. He usually got tender answers. He liked lying against the cinema front best. A man changed the cinema posters and made remarks to him. They were dangerous times. Charlie Chaplin and Lillian Gish came to town. Women did crazy dances, flapping their hands. Music rudely boomed from an organ played by a rude, fat man. Dangerous times. Alan saw only donkeys and carts, old ladies coming from the country, their cheekbones drilled with tales, their eyes choking with the oddity and impedimenta of their experience. An old tinker woman once conversed with Alan for half an hour. She talked gibberish but Alan ascertained she'd been in Sackville Street when the 1916 revolution exploded. The guns were dying down in Dublin. A man of state was shot down emerging from Mass. The face of Alan's mother glimmered harshly. She did not sympathize.

Alan had four brothers though you wouldn't think it. He came second in the family. His father worked at the railway station. His mother had dark hair and stood among photographs of missionary priests and nuns – cousins, sisters, brothers – a premonitory, if sly, look on her face. It was as if she could suddenly by standing still see all manner of disaster. Alan ran from this.

In late summer he would be taken to an aunt's farm in Roscommon. There he heard tales of banshees, headless horsemen, dullaháns – the men who obliged you by throwing buckets of blood in your face when a relative was about to die. Alan would run in the harvest fields. Young men briefly returned from England. One slept in the bed with

3

Alan, Tommy Joe, smoked a cigarette with *élan* and proudly announced, a red hankerchief in his pajama pocket, that he was dating a
princess. Milk was churned.

One day among the stone walls Alan nearly bumped into a young
Spanish cyclist with blue eyes who turned out to have an Irish name.
That was a bit later – in the 1930s when Alan was already wearing long
trousers. Sometimes Alan would return in spring. Rain disturbed the
hydrangeas then. What he would remember from this place too was a
grandfather clock – ticking gently – with the features of a human
being. Alan, small, would often sidle up to it and try to find out if it
had a soul.

When Alan was nine a priest, a cousin, came from Sevilla, sleeping
in the bed with him, flailing his penis as though it was a flowering
bough. Ever after that as he served Mass in white and red Alan would
associate the white with Catholicism's purity and the red with its
converse carnality.

The same year he wrote his first poem. He wrote it in school –
surreptitiously – in pale blue ink. He wrote it on a dark desk carved
with many initials. It was about a snowman.

> Mr. Snowman.
> Mr. Snowman.
> You have pebble eyes.
> A big fat white tummy.
> You hold a broomstick.
> Someone stuck a leaf in your nose.
> A snail crawls on your hat.
> The snail has many colours.
> Do you long for colour Mr. Snowman?
> What do you ask for?
> You say nothing.
> Do you know it already?
> You're going to die Mr. Snowman.
> Do you look with your pebble eyes into your short life?
> Do you long for life Mr. Snowman?
> Is that the gift you ask for?
> But the sun climbs up.
> The day is blue and sunny.
> Very soon there's just your hat left and your pebble eyes.
> I pick them up and take them with me.

He took the poem to an aunt who lived a little outside Athlone.
After reading the poem she opened a book and showed Alan glowing

4

pictures of the nativity. Alan was particularly impressed with the one of the magi, the myrrh, the gold, the frankincense standing out in devotedly special colours.

In adolescence Alan wore most often a mustard coloured jersey and long trousers. The Blueshirts marched in Athlone; their flag of fascism. Priests had picnics with them beside the Shannon. Alan walked by these picnics. He spent much time by the Shannon. He was big and slender. By the Shannon you got lost. He opened books of history. History coloured his mind. He had no friends, no special friends. The world in 1933 was a lonely place. Swans exploded by the Shannon. Swans were the prime part of identification; heroes, martyrs identified with them. In the library Alan read of these heroes. There was war in Spain. A bishop blessed General O'Duffy as he travelled off to Spain with his recruits. Alan's mother muttered about things: sin, sex. A body floated by on the Shannon, an old lady suddenly young like Ophelia. 'What do you want to do in life?' aunts inquired. Alan considered. He wanted to write.

The Christian Brothers had little sympathy for him. He had his dreams though and those dark eyes that infuriated some brothers more than others. 'I will build a house from red wine,' Alan said to himself one day, though he didn't know what he meant. In September 1939 he left a station in Athlone, first waiting fifteen minutes on a platform brimming with marigolds, to train as a teacher in Dublin.

Dublin was a velvet city then; full of soft evenings. Alan got a room in a house on Griffith Avenue. His landlady, a towel on her head, spoke obsessively about Mayo where she was from statues of Mary like Queen Anne dolls discovered undecayed. The bombs came on the North Wall. Alan wrote a novel. This novel came from his childhood, Roscommon, history books. It was called *A Cavalier Against Time*, was about a young man and woman who, during the English civil war, wander around Ireland on a white horse, with her brother and his foster brother, both fair haired, pink skinned, and a Protestant bishop preaching peace. Unfortunately the Protestant bishop and the two boys are killed and the young couple blamed. They flee to her castle in Connemara where they survive on periwinkles and swans. A primeval Irish curse settles on those who eat swans and the lovers are eventually separated, she marrying in Antwerp, he travelling south to Andalucia where he marries a Moroccan girl and lives to old age among the orange trees and the purple Judas trees.

In the time he was working on the novel Alan would often play cards with his landlady. 'You should be studying. You should be studying,' his landlady told him. But while she played cards with him she was glad of his company. She was afraid they'd come back, the bombers. Her son was in Birmingham. Sometimes she'd pray aloud. 'Sacred Heart. Sweet Mary.' The heart of English towns was being torn out. Men walked by cathedrals of ruins. The Queen of Hearts most often came up for Alan.

Some evenings he'd take the bus into town, walk by the placards with the latest news of war, by the waiting women in black, by the threatening Liffey, his long coat on him, a scarf around him. He'd head for a pub and locate himself between literary elders, listening to them talk, smoke in the air, wise words suspended under a stained glass window. No one noticed him too much, as if they associated him with smoke.

In Dublin you browsed, you strolled on the Green. War had given people an appetite and people made gluttons of themselves on what was available in the Metropole. Alan lingered. His novel was in the making.

When his mood was more desolate, full of the landscape of the Bull Wall, of Dollymount shore, Alan would seat himself in the Castle Hotel over a hot port. To think of Athlone was to think of the Shannon, water rising. His family lived on the eastern side, just where narrow terraces converged on the river, the river itself the dividing line between east and west of Ireland. There'd be swans on the Shannon and old matronly women would be drinking a glass of red wine in the hotel.

An elderly writer took an interest in him, brought him to afternoon tea in the Royal Hibernian where there was a negro waiter. Afterwards at tea in Rathgar in the writer's little cottage, over cucumber sandwiches, the old man tried to seduce Alan with his frail hands. Alan was still wearing his coat during tea and left.

'Shocking. Shocking to the world.' The landlady muttered about bombings and cards.

Alan now took trips into the country, walked the hills, looked down on Dublin, in his white shirt ate grass. This was a time alone. He went to films and walked out, preferring to stroll amid the stream of colours. Each face had an identity, an excitement for these moments even if it was only the face of a resident of a red brick, mountainside suburb. One day a face would converge on him from this crowd, he told himself. Eyes took him in. No face reached to grab him. For a short period in 1943 he took to smoking a pipe. He'd sit seriously. People took more notice of him. A girl who worked in a grocery shop became obsessed with him and followed him everywhere. She was a red haired country girl. This gave him more confidence, and he opened his coat as he sat, revealing a white sleeveless jersey with blue rims. You'd swear he was a famous writer or something, with the lazily tied tweed tie above his sweater. Dublin took more notice of him. He became familiar – like the spring leaves on Griffith Avenue. He was absorbed as a feature of the city.

And one night – like a bird screaming on a Midland lake in Ireland – he finished his novel. But he did a strange thing with it. He put it under his arm, brought it home, locked it in a drawer. Maybe he feared its sexual content, couplings between male and male, male and female, swan and swan. Maybe he just ordained life was greater than art and that the art of writing could be obliterated by a single gesture which said it was more important to live than to write. In either case now he was back in Athlone and teaching there he began to change. Maybe it was the war, maybe it was the way women's perfumes merged with the dusk, but whereas in Dublin he'd sit alone over hot port in the Castle Hotel now he began going to dances. In the ballrooms he'd appear in his best clothes. His mother solemnly ironed his white shirts. She reckoned he was seeking a wife.

[2]

The town in which Eileen Carmody grew up was different from Athlone, a dark town beside a wood and a manor house, its main street full of staring and ravaged windows. Protestants were stoned out of this street in 1922, the year after Eileen was born. But many Protestants lingered, playing tennis in white. There was one hotel, one cinema, many pubs. In the 1930s Protestants and Catholics came together to play rugby, to cycle. Eileen, a child, felt left out of the rugby season. Her family lived in the dark oblivion of a lodge house on the edge of the estate beside the woods with an opening onto the Galway Road. The house was full of pictures, clocks, but you couldn't see them for the darkness. Her father worked as gardener for the lady of the manor, wading among the petunias. Sometimes he brought her to the men's billiard club where she spied on films in the cinema below through a hole. Her mother worked for the nuns, cycling to work. Eileen had five brothers and two sisters. She came seventh. From an early age she was accustomed to the smell of male sweat, her brothers, bare armed, digging the garden in vests. She tended the geese and the lilies. At school she was turbulent and stood out. A nun said she offered her up as penance. The same awkward, fat nun in black beat her across the back with a cane and declared she had the legs of a whore. True Eileen had endearingly white legs with red spots. When she was nine a brother crept into bed beside her. 'Darling. Sweetheart,' he whispered, aping Lionel Barrymore or Ramon Novarro sub-titles from the cinema. Eileen clung to a teddy-bear as he fingered her nearly flowering breasts. He returned again and again. She stood in a trance on the side of the main street, like any other Irish girl, in a navy coat and beret to watch the Corpus Christi procession pass, hymns welling up from dried-up old ladies, rose petals falling among yesterday's chocolate papers, red roses exalting profusely bleeding Sacred Heart pictures outside shops with Woodbine cigarette advertisements in the window, but the knowledge she carried at once weighed like a stone in her eyes and soared above that of most Irish girls, placing her with unenviable angels. At fourteen she cycled to a dance, a big farmer throwing her on the ground, ponytail and all, pushing into her. Afterwards she searched among the grass for her red ribbon. Ever after that she'd cycle to dances, giving herself to men, the big and the small, making a montage of them, young men on Irish streets in the 1930s, straw blowing in the breeze, their white shirts billowing over their trousers, their eyes entranced. On nights she didn't go dancing she'd often rise at dawn, go cycling on the Galway Road, light creeping into the rim of the bog, the breeze in her black hair, just to recapture the sensation of returning after a night of lights and fondling hands.

[3]

He smiled when he first saw her though he couldn't properly see her with the sun behind her.

She thought him the most beautiful man she'd ever seen, different from the Micks, the Micheáls, the Michaels, his black hair, pale skin, red lips, a vernacular of gentleness, of hesitation in his smile, coaches with headless horsemen on them emerging from his luminous eyes as in some childhood fairy story.

8

When he eventually saw her it was her dress he noticed, blue with white spots on it.

He said something about Keats. She'd never heard of Keats but she had heard of Mr. Yeats, a Protestant from Dublin who'd died before the war. He asked her to dance and when she accepted he touched her ever so gently on the shoulder, leading her into a marquee from which Glen Miller music issued.

They didn't notice the change from Glen Miller to an old time waltz as they danced. A mongoloid girl in blue sat on a bench, her feet dangling over straw. Young men and young women drank tea out of white mugs with black spots on them. Towards the end of the evening a man made a speech in Gaelic which, roughly translated, stated it was good to see the oppressors who had for so long oppressed this people oppressed themselves.

Alan and Eileen walked by the Shannon. There were blue and orange lights.

She wondered would he contact her?

He told his children about the coming of the Cromwellians to Ireland. Then one day he cycled – penitentially – in a long coat to see her. He brought her to the local hotel which she'd never been to before, the two of them sitting as plump stomached doctors stood chatting under photographs of white togged rugby players.

He didn't contact her for weeks. He continued to tell his children about the coming of the Cromwellians. Tinkers came to her home. Her mother had a tinker man mend a big, long disused saucepan. An ancient tinker woman stood rigid at the door, a myriad ruts, wounded hollows around her yearning eyes, against the blue of the bogline, her hands, delicate with age, clutching a multi-coloured shawl. A young tinker woman with a black shining ponytail sang 'Johnny, lovely Johnny' in the kitchen, a song in which a girl, abandoned by her lover, vows to wreath her brow in a garland of forget-me-nots until he returns. Alan wrote: 'Dear Eileen, Will you come with me to the dance in Athlone on Friday night? I'll be waiting outside the cinema at eight o' clock . . .' She got a lift in a black MG with a party of dance-goers. Crossing the Shannon which divided east from west of Ireland she remembered from school how survivors of the Spanish Armada were led from Galway city on foot, beheaded here, their blood on cold Athlone stone. Alan was waiting outside the cinema in a long coat which made him look half like de Valera and half like a French artist. She wore a black coat that tapered at the waist in a butterfly fashion, a pigeon feather in her black, sidelong beret. They walked through Athlone. There were gashes of red after rain.

9

She came to see him often after that. They sat together in the hotel lounge, young men from the boating club, in black blazers and white trousers, fixated on them. There was something different about them.

He didn't kiss her once, something ritualistic about their relationship – like the host being raised at Mass. She did not know where it was leading to, but she accepted its rudiments.

One day in a café he compared her to Eleanor Laffan, a famous seventeenth-century Irish beauty who'd always suffused her nearly bare breasts in pear blossom smelling perfume and who, despite her many lovers, had fallen in love with the poet and preacher Geoffrey Keating. He condemned her in her presence from the pulpit one day and she in her wrath had the lord president of Munster, one of her lovers, pursue him into the glens of Tipperary. Eileen was afraid her reputation had reached Athlone but in truth Alan only compared her to Eleanor Laffan for beauty.

He came to be with her on the first day of the October fair week in her home town; tinkers on the Green, pie-bald horses. He hugged her waist as he lifted her onto the chairoplanes. Would this ecstasy last?

The first time he mentioned he'd written a novel was as they crossed the Shannon one evening, swans on it. She didn't think of it for a while after that.

He came to see her people, dining on goose and apple sauce, her brothers staring; and she was introduced to his mother, his mother standing among graffiti of missionary priests and nuns, eyeing her beadily.

Alan cycled to take her to the last crossroads dance of the year. An old man with two warts on his nose played a melodion on the platform of a lorry. Girls leaned against a stone wall. In the countryside Protestants collected red apples from gardens outside houses with gilded knockers. Here fires burned in the hills. It was Hallow-e'en.

The first time Alan spoke at length about his novel – describing what Shane O'Neill wore to the court of Elizabeth: saffron; what his warriors wore: wolfskins and leaf-mail – she thought him mad and wanted to walk away, but she stayed and allowed herself be led to a room where, sitting on a couch, she listened to the story of *A Cavalier Against Time*, all the time staring at the drawer where the novel was locked away as though at a terrible wound.

Lorcan O'Mahony was born in Pludd Street near Shoemaker's Tower in Galway city 10 December 1619. His father fittingly was a shoemaker and his mother of Catholic, Gaelic origin. Right from the beginning he had a streak of dark hair on his head which distinguished him.

When he was very small his mother would place him on a stool, she herself standing upright, bun intact, her figure draped in a penitential gown, and tell him tales of Ireland's past, of Gerald Fitzgerald, cripple on horseback, hewn down in Munster, his ghost still flying, eyeless sockets gleaming, his lands confiscated from his posterity, the osprey leaping, pheasant flitting lands of Munster dredged and drained by English newcomers, laburnum instead of the wild hawthorn, and the poet Edmund Spenser, 'that bandy legged dwarf' Lorcan's mother called him, admiring his Goddess Moon in Kilcolman. Everywhere the English were moving in and the Irish being ousted. The bulk of the stories Lorcan's mother told were about the vigil of Ireland, that lady in green with diamonds sewn onto the edges of her dress, for foreign aid. In 1579 James Fitzmaurice landed in Kerry with arms from the pope, wandering about Kerry, proclaiming his descent from Thomas à Becket and waving a banner which showed Christ crowned with thorns and dripping blood, until he was murdered by a Burke. In 1580 Italians and Portuguese ensconced themselves at Dún an Óir before being hacked like seals by English generals. The Spanish Armada approached in 1500 and Lorcan's mother delighted in describing how some of its survivors were beheaded on Saint Augustine's Hill in Galway, their bodies wrapped in linen at night by the people of Galway. One young man escaped the massacre, was sheltered by a local family but his memories proved too much for him and one day, gibbering and mad, in a black cloak, he walked into the hills to be devoured by O'Flahertys or wild boars. The Spanish made a final unsuccessful bid on Ireland in 1601 and after that the last great earls of Ulster, O'Neill and O'Donnell, left, their red and watery eyes witnessing a vision of Christ over Croagh Patrick as they passed that mountain in an untrustworthy vessel; their boat chased by the English outside Galway; their bodies lying now in the Franciscan Convent of San Pietro in Montorio, Rome; their sculpted hands in repose under Raphael's *Transfiguration*; the soul of Ireland dead among the burnished golds of Renaissance Italy.

The effects of this death were felt in Galway as Lorcan was growing up. Once known as the 'Thebes of the Western World' now its population looked wistfully to an ocean which no longer readily brought wine and silk from Spain, ivory from Africa, spices from India. Merchants went by holding their flagging bellies. A Catholic town, it had been the first to prostrate itself at the feet of Protestantism. The people of Galway had allowed the lord deputy to tie his horses in Saint Nicholas' Church in 1534. The Gaelic chieftains had kissed the ring of Elizabeth on a gold cushion here. Its hinterland always having been denied, now that hinterland moved closer, men in wolfskins, women lean like starving calves rubbing shoulders with the city. In 1596 O'Donnell had surrounded the town but was driven off by a mad nun who had threatened to curse him with syphilis. Now the terms of siege had changed. Although a Catholic queen reigned, nuns hurried like dormice at dawn and priests celebrated Mass among rocks where seals were slaughtered at Michaelmas. Religion was the bartering table, and the traditional but waning wealth of Galway the prize. A woman played a strange tune on a flageolet in Blake's Lane and dust settled on the black cloak of a blind woman.

To escape this unease Lorcan would run through the streets of Galway in the early morning, nearly stumbling once or twice into an Italian merchant who prodded along with a diamond topped stick, bypassing the Cataracts where men fished with spears, fleeting along a beach where donkeys carried cargoes of seaweed, confronting the ocean where he expected a Spanish vessel to rise, sails ethereal like fairy goblets, though all that usually emerged above the horizon was cloud formations like Ferdia, like Oisín.

When he was nine his mother brought him to a place of pilgrimage in the north, clinging to him on a mule's back; Gaelic tribes crossing their path with lean, shaggy cattle; charred spots on the hills where corn was burned to separate the wheat from the chaff; women on stools plucking the wool from sheep's backs. They crossed in a currach to an island where they crawled on bare knees over stones; rising at dawn, penance done, to dance to bagpipe music. What Lorcan would remember about this place however was a gate to Hell closed down by decree of a pope because the visions of those who entered were so tormenting: devils warming their naked backsides over quivering fires, bishops with faces half of toadstools and croziers of fungus eaten trees, remorseless personal memories.

His mother and father were swept away in a plague the following year and Lorcan was adopted by an aunt who'd turned Protestant to marry an English merchant, one of the class who'd come to take over the apple blossom crowded, brook gurgling monasteries of Ireland. This lady did not look unlike Ireland herself, jewels sewn onto the edges of her red dress, raven hair in a bun, an eloquent distance between her pale breasts. She and her husband lived in a Dutch red brick house with dormer windows near Athenry but because of the many sieges they moved into the house in Pludd Street, retiling the floor.

Lorcan was taught Euclid by a Protestant minister in black, standing upright in a small room, hands behind his back. More often than not he managed to escape, chasing butterflies down Martin's Mill Lane, overhearing the voice of a teacher in the Gaelic school of Alexander Lynch. 'In the year 30 after Christ some fifteen of his followers landed in West Connaught with five geese, two chickens, a pig. They set about building a house near a stream between two hills and preaching his word.' Young men lay on rushes on the floor. A solitary light came through a lattice window.

In 1634 Wentworth, the lord deputy, rode into Galway on a mule, grinning like an Italian puppet. Already there were rumours. He sat in the castle of the Earl of Clanricarde in Portumna, feet on the oak table. He was after land for the king. He had three Galway lawyers look into the king's title in Galway and when they found against the king he had them thrown into jail, one of them perished, and the other two on their release assigned one third of the lands of Galway to the king. A dead whale lay on a beach and Lorcan's aunt died.

She died screaming. Keening women waited, their turnip faces grinning, a proselyte about to go down to Hell. White horses with black plumes on their heads cantered at her funeral and ran away with the coffin. Lightning stood in the air, a tableau, and the sea raged against an English garrison.

A young man journeyed up to Dublin in the 1630s, haunted by the antiquated voice of a teacher in the Gaelic school of Alexander Lynch and by the red scarf of one of the new English preachers; the teacher describing early Christians bringing fragments of Christ's cross to Connemara and the preacher's hands raised to the paltry Atlantic sun, his black figure trembling in one of Galway's squares as his sermon boasted of a new age based on love and brotherhood and the sun.

A student in black, Lorcan sat in a room in Trinity College with a hawk. It was not uncommon to see soldiers chase Carmelite priests caught saying Mass through the streets or to hear Protestant bishops in Christ Church rail against the Catholic population: 'Happy shall he be who taketh and dasheth thy children against the storm', to see men urinating in the corners, clerics getting drunk in the cellars below, while by Saint Patrick's Cathedral the gentlefolk of Dublin tripped over pigs' guts from the nearby tanneries to hear more sober sermons.

Wherever he went, through the streets filled with gooseberries in early summer, with Malahide oysters in winter, in the taverns overrun with actors from the New Theatre in Werburgh Street and whores, Lorcan could still hear them, two voices, a direction. A fat, drunken chancellor was driven in a carriage from County Cork to Trinity and Lorcan took off for Italy, a typical student of the time. A student from Oxford insulted him on the Ponte Vecchio for being Irish. He was assailed by fumes of portraits of young men fumigated to rid them of typhoid. Jesuits, seeking to convert him, chased him amid the storm of gold of the Vatican Square, cloaks raised above their heads. But he couldn't stop remembering and, on the force of an intuition, he returned to Galway, swept on a white horse into the Connemara countryside, past eddying tides of red deer, until he came to the castle of Eleanor O'Keefe near Renvyle.

Her people had left Kerry in the previous century, driven out by the English, departing from the hills rustling with red dresses and resounding with the 'Te Deum', crossing the Shannon in currachs made of cows' hides, birds of winter and snow dangling, arriving here, a rainbow. Swans hovered in the bay behind and little boats took off from a gully to larger boats, which hurried to Europe. Eleanor, a red-headed girl with eyes that gleamed the secretive green of dark bottles in Galway wineshops, stood at the door as though she'd been expecting him for a long time.

Apart from Eleanor, only her brother lived here with his Welsh foster-brother, both albinos, the two of them sleeping together on a mat of rushes. Their faces, eyes, piece upon frail piece, looked to the sea, querulously. Priests came from and went to Europe, little, bald, agitated men ruminating over words left by an early Christian sect who had frequented this area. 'If you give birth to what is within you, you will be saved. If you do not give birth to what is within you, you will perish.' Eleanor refilled their glasses with red wine. The two boys stared at cards which showed witches and minstrels, and the priests hurried off to Europe, their findings under their arms, fearful lest their investigations were not completed before an oncoming calamity.

Lorcan went back and forth, becoming Eleanor's lover, the two of them sleeping together on the kitchen floor, a brook running through, a Brigid's cross over the door, rushes in the eaves, their love-making fragmentary, the feathers, wings, lineaments of swans.

Early in 1641 there was a deluge of rats in Ireland. Later in the year a manifestation of caterpillars in Moycullen, a sure sign. In October the Catholics of Ulster rose – rumours of babies roasting on spits – the people of Galway declared for the king but later, the governor away, seized the garrison. They surrendered at the entreaties of the Earl of Clanricarde. The English, however, were not satisfied with a simple submission and came in seventeen ships, burning the bones of the dead at Saint Dominic's Monastery, murdering lone boatmen. The people of Galway rose again, seizing the garrison again, ordering two cannons from France, sending delegates to the new Catholic parliament in Kilkenny.

In 1643 the churches were reopened, a giant cross erected on Great Middle Street for the Corpus Christi procession – priests in red and white treading on roses of Sharon, singing the 'Te Deum' in unison – a huge, unwieldy alligator.

That was the point at which Lorcan, Eleanor, the two boys left the castle in Connemara, veering north, collecting a Protestant bishop in Mayo, encircling the north coast, all the time preaching a gospel based on the pacifism of early Christians in Connemara and the teachings of new English preachers as compounded for Lorcan, by candlelight in a Dublin inn, by a young English actor from the New Theatre in Werburgh Street, who spoke of the dispossessed of England stirring among the fens, the forests, reclaiming the earth. Wherever they went they heard stories of atrocities in the recent rebellion – naked men, women and children pushed into icy waters, pregnant women tied to chairs as dartboards, pious women buried alive in potato fields. They passed a spot where a young man had waited helplessly in the previous century as his family were slaughtered on a nearby island, swans standing in the air, a forewarning graffiti. They rested near a castle where a Protestant bishop had been buried by the O'Neills and, so loved by them, lamented with kettle drums and bagpipes though they had caused his death by imprisoning him for a winter in a castle with cannon ball holes in the walls. They warmed themselves over vagrants' fires – Lorcan's face lucid with flame – listening to stories of the old days, hot wine with ginger, nutmeg and burnt sugar. The two boys held hands, drinking water out of stone goblets. The Protestant bishop murmured in his sleep. Eleanor slept on Lorcan's shoulder as he sat awake. They were welcomed by a gentle family, marching up an avenue of cypress trees, the fires squashed out, the stones cold, the lady of the house wandering about in a lace nightdress, reciting her childhood prayers. A wandering lute player entertained them with 'Lady Hunsun, Her Galliard', and they moved on towards Dublin on roads naked men, women and children had converged upon in the recent rebellion.

They spent the winter in Dublin when the Liffey broke its banks, playing perilous games of chess in an inn near Oxmanton, heading south again come spring, passing English soldiers warming themselves with ikons of mother and child thrown into fires, overhearing Irish soldiers with knife-edge eyes move among the trees, encountering a landscape smouldering with war and crawling with lost women and children.

Near Castlecomer they had the most terrible sight of all. Under a pigmy tree an old woman ate a baby as though it was chicken bones.

They preached on, young man and woman on the same white horse, two boys in love, an unwieldy Protestant bishop, a strange circus which prevailed against a landscape of famine and war, drawing an audience of women holding children, of men with mouths blackened from eating nettles, disappearing again, leaving their audience more confused than before on the outskirts of some village.

They were left alone until they came to North Cork and there the two boys, lagging behind, were murdered, their bodies found hugging one another, sheep's bodies tarnished in blood, and later the Protestant bishop was killed in an ambush. Lorcan and Eleanor, surveying him, a disarray of vestments, knew they'd be blamed but they rode on. By now they were legendary, young man and woman on the same white horse preaching peace, a spectral pair. People waited on the outskirts of villages for them. But their audience betrayed them by dying. They wandered for days and weeks through black bog and forest, past clumps of red berries, climbing hills slit by lake and pool, challenging cloud, affronted by raucous jackdaws, swathed in soft rain. They found no one and eventually preached to one another. Eleanor lying on Lorcan's shoulder was hit by a solitary flake of snow on a mountaintop one day and they fled to her castle in Connemara which was already pillaged by war.

There they survived on periwinkles picked from the shore and swans killed by a musket Lorcan had purchased from a gibbering beggar. Swans fell from the air, white corpses. They approached tentatively. A primeval Irish curse settles on those who eat swan's meat but they feasted on the delicious fragments, roasting them on spits. Eleanor smiled as Lorcan handed her morsels, her red hair flaming against the fading Atlantic sun. Come twilight they told stories to one another over the fire, Lorcan retelling the tales of Homer and Virgil, Eleanor filling in the gaps of history, describing how King John when he came to Ireland met Ruanus who had lived since the time of the Flood and how Solinus, the Roman historian, had thought the Irish Sea to be navigable for only a few weeks in summertime. At night they slept close, reverberations of wine from the cellar below, the sea pounding in, sounds of war coming closer. In the morning they'd rise, kill more swans, devouring them. They spent a winter here and a spring. A Spanish wreck magically washed up, and whales went south. Eleanor walked the shore as though she'd had a surfeit of wine. Eventually they tired of their diet and took refuge in Galway. That winter it was hit by a plague and they followed the townsfolk into the hills where they waited until Our Lady's Day when the plague lifted and the people returned like dreamers to a town where grass grew on the doorsteps.

Events in Ireland were furious and hard to follow. One day Butler rode into Kilkenny, accepted as leader by the Catholic Confederates, the deeds of his ancestors proclaimed on the walls. The next day the spit-fire Rinuccini swept in, incarcerating those who had supported Butler, declaring himself leader in an upsurge of red robes. Munster was being devastated and Connaught laid waste, right up to the point it was waste anyway. Then Cromwell came.

Lorcan and Eleanor, living in the house in Pludd Street, Lorcan's uncle dead, heard the stories with trepidation. Drogheda was ransacked, gentlewomen hacked as they proffered their jewels on their knees, pregnant women with swords through their wombs, hands clasping mother of pearl rosaries in the mud, men, women and children perishing in Saint Peter's Church, the flame of gunpowder merging with the scarlet of a cavalier's cloak and the rage of blood on the Boyne.

In Wexford monks rose from the massacre into the sky, resting on clouds, their hands piously joined in prayer. In Cloughoughter the Catholic general Eóghan Ruadh Ó'Néill, died on the ground, last revealing the Dominican garb under his military uniform. In Clonmacnoise Catholic bishops cried out against Cromwell at a synod among the ruins. But the Cromwellians forged on. Limerick was besieged, men hanged at its gate. Then Galway surrounded.

Lorcan stood over Eleanor as she sat, like any lord with his lady in a portrait of the time, except that their clothes were peeling and their skin festering.

Priests raised the host among congregations of rats and a whole convent of nuns took to witchcraft in desperation.

Lorcan and Eleanor knew they had to get out before it was too late. Ladies swept in and out of inns, their noses in the air, consumptive children holding their trains, the ladies oblivious to the stench of corpses because of the position of their noses and the profusion of perfumes which surrounded them. A Quaker lady was murdered by O'Flaherty youths as she knelt at prayer on a prie-dieu, her head used as a football. A ship bearing corn nearly broke through the blockade but was offset. Some men seeking cattle outside the city gates were murdered. Then the siege broke. The Parliamentarians marched in, Palm Sunday 1652.

Eleanor managed to escape dressed as a soldier, marching out with other soldiers, wolfhounds alongside them, kettle drums beating, a solitary bagpiper lamenting them into exile as a ship waited. Lorcan slipped out the opposite direction in a priest's garb, encountering the native Irish as they flooded west before Cromwell's men, witnessing their weddings and their wakes, among stones, among brooks, an absolute defiance to fate. He was captured as a priest, imprisoned in white in Inishbofin while awaiting transportation to the West Indies, again escaped, this time in a currach with a bishop who'd held an ikon of mother and child from Saint Nicholas's Church in Galway under the clay of his cabin. Starting off from a nearby island, step by step, Lorcan got as far as Scotland, crossing Scotland, reaching Europe. There he began his search for Eleanor. They'd made a pact. She wore his onyx ring. They'd married under a white hawthorn tree beside black bog water in the presence of the two boys and the Protestant bishop.

In Paris, Irish noblemen walked by with holes in their hose and Butler, the flaxen haired, was rumoured to live on a pistole a week. Crowds surged angrily around the coach of a sparrow-like cardinal and Lorcan moved on to Brussels. There Irish noble-ladies were ensconced in the Convent of the Feuillantines. He headed east. In the Palatine May Day was still celebrated, flowers about cows' udders, fires in the hills. The further east he went the more demented puppets on village greens became. All the time a picture formed, that of a portrait of a young man holding a medallion remembered from Italy. In Poland, clouds of war raging, he turned back. Back in Paris Irish noblemen had become drunker and more slovenly, one of them insulting Lorcan from a sidewalk. An Irish noble family, fallen on good times, invited him to their home, feeding him and clothing him. The young girl of the house, albino herself, played the harpsichord, singing 'Thugamar Féin A Samradh Linn' – 'We bring the Summer with Us' – and the lady of the house mourned the old days though no one knew what or where the old days were any more. Lorcan stood over the harpsichord, glass of red wine in his hand in a familiar gesture, and at the end of the evening a dwarfed servant handed him an address. In Antwerp he found Eleanor, bedecked in jewellery, married to a merchant, not wanting to see him.

He thrust south, all the time thinking of the stories they had told one another around Ireland to send one another to sleep, of young

Irish soldiers all around Europe telling the same stories over camp-fires to keep one another awake for the next battle, of swans falling from the air, a vanquished heritage.

One day he mounted a hill, saw the sea and heard a flamenco song, the voice of the flamenco merging with the lamentation of women in Galway and the music of a curlew as a young man and woman on horseback, two boys, a Protestant bishop passed a lake in Ireland. Lorcan O'Mahony had found a home.

He married a Moroccan girl, started a timber business in Sevilla, lived until the Bourbons came to power. An old man, nearly blind, he'd sit in a garden among the orange trees and the purple Judas trees listening to his grandchildren play, his eyes still aflame, the blue of the sea round Saint Macdara's Island on a fine summer's morning. Irish priests would come tripping from the Royal College of the Noble Irish in Salamanca with the latest ill-tidings from Ireland; Aughrim, the coming of the magpies from Wales, the penal laws, the accession of the bonhav faced queen. But all the time his mind would not be on war and devastation but on a young man and woman on a white horse preaching peace and how the years had plucked out their idealism and mutilated their love like a portrait of a young man with the eyes torn out.

[5]

Alan Mulvanney did not look unlike a portrait himself November 1943 when his coat was off, in a scarlet V-necked jersey, a shining white shirt always persuasively open at the neck, a green tie striped with yellow and red. Against red velvet hotel couches, against wooden bar pews he sat erect, a dignity and even a derangement about him.

An old man with a toothbrush moustache marched in the middle of the streets of Athlone, giving the Nazi salute. A Jewish family living on the Dublin Road was driven out of town. Two Protestant sisters in the country opened their house as a hospital for cats, they themselves dressed in nurses' uniforms. The romance of Alan Mulvanney and Eileen Carmody settled. Eileen still did not know where it was leading to – an altar, a mound of roses, a bed? – but she trusted its direction. They complemented one another with coats, scarves.

One Sunday evening Eileen picked up a dust smothered book from the top of a radio and read her first poem.

When we two parted
In silence and tears,
Half broken hearted
To sever for years,
Pale grew thy cheek and cold,
Colder thy kiss;
Truly that hour foretold
Sorrow to this.

The dew of the morning
Sat chill on my brow –
It felt like the warning
Of what I feel now,
Thy vows are all broken,
And light is thy fame;
I hear thy name spoken,
And share in its shame.

They name thee before me,
A knell to my ear;
A shudder comes o'er me –
Why wert thou so dear?
They know not I know thee,
Who knew thee too well: –
Long, long shall I rue thee,
Too deeply to tell.

In secret we met –
In silence I grieve,
That thy heart could forget,
Thy spirit deceive.
If I should meet thee
After long years,
How should I greet thee? –
With silence and tears.

The same evening Alan in his scarlet jersey, white open-necked shirt, green tie, pored over the Bible. 'Intreat me not to leave thee, or to return from following after thee: for whither thou goest, I will go; and where thou lodgest I will lodge: thy people shall be my people, and thy God my God.' Next morning he rose to find Hamburg had been bombed again.

A brother of Eileen's took off to England. Her mother fell on her knees on the stone steps of the lodge house. He was going to be murdered by Adolf Hitler.

Rugby players ran riot on the mental hospital grounds in Eileen's town. Mad people stared out from behind the bars of windows. Fog came to Athlone. It stilled things.

The eighth of December was the Feast of the Immaculate Conception of Mary, therefore a school holiday, and Alan requested Eileen to accompany him to Dublin. She'd been to Galway on a few ragged familial visits, never to Dublin. She cut out a new frock for the occasion, finding the pattern in a pre-war magazine. Foxes crackled in the wood outside. Her mother leaned back and spoke of childhood, one of the first times she spoke freely. Was it a sign she was growing old? Anyway, these days were days of change.

December 8 was a fine day. She took a train as far as Athlone. Alan was waiting on the platform, a figure in a long fawn belted coat, hands in his pockets, the blue air reeling about him. Urchin-like boys offered news of the war, their pale fingers crushing newspaper photographs of fresh blasts of smoke. Alan got on the train. A woman in black beside them, a mother-of-pearl headed pin in her black velvet hat, muttered about the war. A boy in white served them coffee. There were rainbows in the Midland bogs. Men, women, children got on and off the train slowly like refugees. Alan said he came on the wrong day, that his mother had hoped he'd be born today, the Feast of the Immaculate Conception.

'And straight I will repair to the Curragh of Kildare.' White horses cantered by on the Curragh. Alan leaned against the seat opposite, white shirt showing above fawn coat, his face smiling. Suddenly they were in Dublin, his city.

It could be argued that Galway was his city, Galway on a fine morning, Galway where swans lifted themselves as though on magical stilts from quayside steps in early morning, flapping their wings, Galway where white Spanish terraces ran riot, where women in black cloaks and red petticoats observed the sea, philosophically smoking pipes, the Galway of *A Cavalier Against Time*, the Galway his mother had brought him to once or twice, an adolescent boy in a mustard coloured jersey. But Dublin was the place where all mornings had merged for him into a single morning when he woke and decided to write a novel. This morning Dublin was very blue. The Liffey swept to the outside world. Out there were bombs and people preoccupied

21

with a curious world of sin, if you were to believe Irish priests. Eileen fingered the white green-rimmed cups in Bewley's Oriental Café in Westmoreland Street. She took off her navy coat for the first time to reveal her cornflower blue dress with its lace collar. Even Alan was dazzled. Women in black from big houses in the country sat over bacon and eggs and old priests sublimated over cherry buns.

The first place they visited was the National Museum where Alan had researched his novel, viewing pistoles, half-pistoles, groats, Venetian glass, two headed drinking cups behind glass cases as though they had been the matter of a great novel. Looking at her reflection in a glass case, again her navy coat on, Eileen wondered for the umpteenth time why this charade existed, why this novel was locked away. Alan had his own answer that day: a blind accordionist playing 'When Irish Eyes Are Smiling' on O'Connell Bridge, swaying from side to side, a little bent old lady in purple talking about her rotten neighbours to herself as she hobbled along Grafton Street, postcards of Vermeers and Rembrandts in shops by the Liffey; this was the city of his youth, a place closed off. That novel represented this city. Perhaps some day he'd resurrect the novel. Perhaps some day he'd write a new novel and show it to the world, but for now he stared into a glass case containing wine goblets and swords which showed his reflection, curly black hair, his fawn, open hanging coat. He was still young. There were still roads to travel. There was still time to reveal the space shrouded by trees on Griffith Avenue, a young man in a white shirt at a typewriter, the sun pouring in, the leaves in bloom outside.

Next they looked in on the National Library where Alan wrote some of his novel, reverentially standing as old ladies wrote treatises on the Battle of Aughrim.

They visited Stephen's Green where Alan pointed out an old astrologer with a white goatee who was speaking to the ducks. All around were weeping willows and ducks. Eileen stood as elegantly as possible.

They lunched at the Metropole. All the day Alan was becoming younger and younger. Eileen wanted to reach to the youth in Alan's face, stroke it with a black velvet glove. But each time she made a manifest gesture this quality receded in Alan.

Eileen, a little drunk, spoke to herself in the mirror in the ladies. 'Now don't wobble, Eileen, be good.' She fixed her hat at the same time, finding the right angle with tremendous difficulty.

The blind accordionist on O'Connell Bridge was playing 'I'll take you home again Kathleen' as they got a bus to the zoo. Eileen had seen most of the animals before in visiting circuses, not the rhinoceros. Alan hilariously identified each of them with an Irish politician or prelate of the time. By the seal pond, a fat black seal whining behind him, spontaneously, red wine on his lips, the whine of the seal becoming more human, Alan kissed her on the lips. She'd never forget that kiss. He withdrew. The sun was Arctic on the polar bears.

They had tea in the Shelbourne lounge before leaving. Eileen was beginning to speak with an upper class accent in the course of the day. Here upper society brushed around. Darkness was falling on Stephen's Green. They walked to the train. Crowds were pushing out of churches. The Liffey ran velvet to the sea. Eileen said goodbye to her first glimpse of the outside world, a red patch over the split where the Liffey breaks into the sky. On the crowded train home, lights in country houses, a woman in black beside them recited the rosary in Irish under her breath 'Se do bheath a Mhuire.' An ancient language broke through.

The Shannon rose high in December, swans in shadows. After his display of emotion in Dublin Alan retreated. There was red in his eyes and red rims about them. He wore his white, sleeveless, blue-rimmed jersey. His head lay deeply back in seats. Leningrad was being fought over by the Germans and the Russians. An ancient and elegant city was in mortal peril. Already hundreds of thousands had died. Leningrad became Dublin, became a city of youth, of sacred things. The nature of sacredness itself was being contested in the world.

Alan spoke obsessively of lovers, citing examples from history, Edmund Spenser and Elizabeth Boyle, Geoffrey Keating and Eleanor Laffan, even Cromwell and Elizabeth Bourchier. He spoke of his first poem, a snowman fading away. He spoke of art itself, a perishable thing, a Venetian glass in a glass case in a Dublin museum, a young man's reflection in the glass case, a would-be artist, a would-be human being. He spoke of the war, of suffering, of the pointlessness of it all. Another of Eileen's brothers slipped away from home, this time to Limerick.

Finally, in this time of war, Alan began to have recourse to history, telling tales of history. Athlone brightened up. But something dug into Alan, the pointlessness of his historical images.

Eileen thought of him one evening, in his red jersey. She thought of a portrait of a young man holding a medallion in a picture Alan had showed her. She thought of Lorcan O'Mahony, holding up a glass of red wine in Galway. She saw Alan as one of these people. She wanted to take him and kiss his lips, red wine on hers. She longed for him now.

How do you make the connection between art and life? Alan wondered. For a moment in Athlone Eileen thought he resembled mad people behind bars in the mental hospital in her town.

Alan wrote a play for his children, a Gaelic nativity play, little children in emerald running about under mistletoe. One little girl made a speech. 'We have come from the courts of Ulster, passing hills of many fires, to seek a child who is born among stone. This child shall change the course of the sea, the imprints of the sand, the direction of the breezes. This child will breathe love on the palms of our hands.' Two days after Christmas there was to be a dance in Athlone. Alan and Eileen decided to go.

A tiny old woman in black, black beret on her head, pushed a pram through the holly in the Blackwoods near Eileen's home on Christmas Eve, collecting firewood. Candles burned in the windows of country houses outside Athlone. More than one tramp was turned away from the doors of these houses.

Eileen went to midnight Mass with her brothers, sisters, parents. Alan went to Mass on Christmas morning with his mother. Eileen had turkey for dinner, Alan goose. Eileen paid a customary visit to the convent crib with her mother, the two of them waiting in the darkness, Eileen in a black coat and black beret, her mother penit-antly holding a handbag, pink light on the infant Jesus, a nun's silver star above him, a swish of robes and a rattle of beads in the air as a nun presently approached and ushered them into a room where, as it was Christmas, they were given tea and lady-like slivers of cake. Alan visited the crib in Athlone with his mother. He looked on the child Jesus and wondered at his vulnerability; how could there be birth in a world of war, of annihilation? He thought of a Protestant bishop dining with the O'Neills, his captors in Cavan on a Christmas Day in the 1640s, for one day a warm fire and hot wine. He looked at the infant and was confused by the paradox, bombs, genocide, the mutilation of children. His mother whispered her venial prayers. He wanted to take the chalk child home but it stolidly remained part of the crib, Athlone, Christmas 1943.

Alan and Eileen went to the dance as arranged but Alan's father being with his sister in Roscommon and his mother having taken his brothers to a pantomime in Dublin, Eileen led him home early. In a room full of photographs of priests and nuns, an orange light on, she took off his clothes, one by one, his underpants, bid him kneel, held his head against her waist. Then she took him by the hand, indicated the way, laid him on a bed, removed her own clothes, bent to kiss his mouth, chest, genitals. They were wounded things, his genitals,

24

purple, red. She took them in her mouth and then rose, kissing his mouth again, lingering over it, savouring its smell, toothpaste, grapes, chocolate, kissed his nipples again, took his genitals again, limp in her mouth, became wilder, a goat digging the earth, pressing him, forcing him, confusing him. But Alan just lay there, eyes on the ceiling. After a while she realized. Her stockings lay on a chair. His red jersey lay on another chair in the other room. Alan lay back, his eyes on the ceiling, his mind on dreams of history.

Afterwards it would have more impact for her than war, massacres, concentration camps or, eventually, twin clouds over cities in the Far East. A month later she said goodbye to Alan by the Shannon on a night it was just beginning to snow. She walked her way. She heard again a blind accordionist on a bridge in Dublin. The river was leading now to the outside world.

[6]

After Eileen was gone Alan went on teaching. Little girls loved his blackberry curls and little boys loved his white shirts. There were photographs of robot-like priests and nuns eaten in Africa on the wall, requisite ikons of the time, and an inscription from Paracelsus by a prize winning pupil, 'He who knows nothing, loves nothing. He who can do nothing understands nothing. He who understands nothing is worthless. But he who understands also loves, notices, sees . . . The more knowledge is inherent in a thing the greater the love . . . Anyone who imagines all fruits ripen at the same time as the strawberries knows nothing about grapes.' Alan's favourite subject was the coming of the Cromwellians to Ireland and his children never tired of hearing about it. He'd always look to the Shannon before beginning, wander around the class, hands in his pockets, stopping to toss back a curl as he described how Oliver Cromwell played chess with a Jesuit priest in Dublin in August 1649. It was not uncommon in Athlone at the time to hear little girls munching chocolate discuss Cromwell's home life outside sweetshops in the rain-soaked streets after school.

He developed a reputation for literariness and as such was called to advise the drama group on difficult matters. He himself directed Strindberg's *The Father* in 1947 and it won many prizes at drama festivals. During this experience he formed one of the rare friendships

25

of his life, with a blond, slightly balding bank clerk from Dublin. This boy was son of a revolutionary gunned down on the Republican side in Dublin during the civil war. Together the boy and Alan sat on the red velvet couches of Athlone lounges. But friendships fade. Alan was thrown up again on the skyline, a solitary figure in a long coat walking the edge of the town, regularly appearing in people's dreams among the town's furthest lights.

'22 January 1949. I feel so alone. Is there anyone in the whole of Ireland who can understand? I feel I am falling, falling through the air but there is nowhere to land.'

In September 1949 his mother died. He sat over the corpse. Tall candles flamed, unreal against the harvest sunshine in the fields outside. She looked southern, severe, in death, hands joined on her black cardigan, her nose sticking up. Alan sat over the corpse, a child.

The following year he had his notorious nervous breakdown. He became obsessed with Our Lady, Queen of Ireland, keeping his children in after class, describing one particular statue of Mary left in the bogs near Athlone since the penal laws, caressed by bog cotton, still drawing a flotsam of wet pilgrims as it had in the penal days.

He was given leave from school in October 1950 and travelled to Italy. He was still wearing his long coat when he descended from the plane. A nun brushed past him. 'I wonder how Sister Aloysius is?' she said to a companion. There were dark glasses on Alan's nose.

On the way into Rome nuns gabbled about homes in Mayo or Roscommon, far flung farmhouses, sapling farm children. They passed a half fallen façade with a poster of a bullfight, a flaring red cloth in a toreador's hand, advertising a film.

Alan got a hotel in Trastevere, the woman of the hotel giving him a table in the cobbled square outside where he sat drinking red wine. He began a postcard 'Dear –'. There was no one to write to.

The first place he went to was the graves of O'Neill and O'Donnell in the Franciscan Convent of San Pietro in Montorio, tracing the fundamental richness of his own imagery, but the sweaty air proved distasteful and he left, going instead to Keats's grave in the Protestant Cemetery, standing there, his short-sleeved shirt red, dark glasses on his nose, the vines broiled at his feet, the sun sweeping through the cypress trees. 'Here lies one whose name is writ in water.' Alan wept.

Rome was like a house after a supper. War had provided the feast and people were glad to be alive. Women chattered at doorways. Chickens scattered in front of boys on scooters. G.Is swayed by in cisterns of light. Boys stood at doorways, their eyes a realm of darkness.

Alan walked on. He walked for days and weeks, wandering down steps, up alleyways. The Indian summer increased in dimension, glistening on his arms below his red, short-sleeved shirt, marked by black patterns, obliterating the expression on his face under his dark glasses. Here Keats lived. Here Keats saw a princess who had posed half naked for a famous statue. There were green patches of lichen on white walls. The time came for him to go and he stayed. Finally Alan realized the true nature of search. It wasn't what you were searching for that was important. It was the search itself.

At night he'd sit outside. German music sounded from somewhere. Stars tumbled into the Tiber. Boys waited in dark alleyways, merrows in Irish legend, the creature half female, half fish who lured you to your doom. Alan's fist tightened on a bottle of red wine.

He familiarized himself with cobbled squares where fountains merged into one another, crossing them in a newly bought orange T-shirt, his hair newly cropped. A woman turned sideways to look at him. A little girl offered him a lick of her ice-cream. He accepted.

The woman of the hotel became friendlier, sitting with him in the square outside at night, telling him, in English picked up from Americans, about the Nazis in Sicily where she was from. Alan reciprocated with stories of the Black and Tans, priests' bodies in bushes, priests dragged by horses across fields.

The Indian summer changed, an arc over the Tiber. Alan strolled alongside it.

He sat in his room in his orange T-shirt, drinking red wine, wondering how he could ever have lived in it, a town of grey spires. Bottles accumulated.

A woman held up a last bunch of purple Saint Michael's daisies and an old man handed him a worn postcard of mother and child by the Tiber.

He bought a suit. An American man mistook him for Montgomery Clift on the Appian Way, and an old Italian man raised a glass of red wine to him. Alan smiled back. But by now he was used to admiration and he walked on, overhearing fragments of gossip about marriages, affairs, film premières; sat with a German woman who'd been through a concentration camp, with an elderly Englishman who asked him if he'd been to Cambridge. Alan said he hadn't. One night Alan walked too far, into a cold dawn, paper handkerchiefs shuffling on aisles of white, empty tables, stubs of red wine at the end of glasses.

In spite of his friendship with the woman of the hotel he shifted hotels, fearing they would come and get him: the doctors, the headmasters, the little girls with bog cotton hair. It was all his mother's legacy of course, the suits, the drink. Winter in this city was like winter nowhere else. Near his new hotel an old man sold roasted chestnuts. Alan often stood beside him, hands in his trousers' pockets, a giant multi-coloured leaf by his feet.

'Once upon a time a boy lived in a town where storks didn't fly.' Sometimes the past composed itself like a fairy story. In November a boy moved in, staying briefly, moving out again. In the space in which he'd held him there was an imaginary medallion. Alan stared at the wall.

One morning he woke and found it had snowed, nuns treading over the Vatican Square fearful lest they should perish, black dots on white.

He celebrated his birthday with wine. His one cherished memory of Athlone was of swans but even they seemed lachrymose. The bottles were like friends now.

He met Father O'Hehirly under Michelangelo's *Creation*. Father O'Hehirly was a red bearded man from County Mayo who lived in the Irish College. They had a cappuccino in a nearby trattoria. Very soon they found they shared a mutual interest – Irish history.

Father O'Hehirly was from one of the most far flung places in Mayo. He had four brothers, all 'lusty leaping hurling players' he called them. They lived by the edge of the sea. There were gulls. He had a mother who, if you were to believe him, always had steaming cabbage and bacon on a tray in her hand. But his prime interest in life was Irish history. He brought Alan to see the museum in the Irish College. The flag of the Irish Brigade. Their motto 'God and our Lady and Rory O'More' written on it. Their boots lying there, black and brown. Their wine goblets. Young men who'd left Ireland for the armies of Europe. Alan thought of his ancestor Lorcan O'Mahony wandering Paris without wine and of a moment in a museum in Dublin, his reflection on a glass case. Walking home from the Irish College one evening Alan saw a young woman sitting in a doorway washing her feet in a basin. 'As I walked out through Galway city at the hour of twelve in the night, who should I meet but a Spanish lady washing her feet by broad moonlight.'

Why this obsession with history? Why this novel in a drawer? Why the physical good looks, black curling hair, red lips? Alan didn't know. But he shouldn't have accepted the invitation of Father O'Hehirly – Anthony as he liked to be called – to dinner in the Irish College on Christmas Day.

Early one morning an American woman smiled at him. There

was a leaf between them as both stood still. The American woman reckoned she was smiling at someone famous.

In the days immediately prior to Christmas the windows of trattorias were even more fogged. Alan sat alongside them. The idea of another novel was coming – slowly. This time he wouldn't put it in a drawer.

'Rome, Christmas morning, 1950. City of martyrs, of idealists, of self-sacrifice, of purity. Pope Pius XII, cloaked in red, carried on a gold sedia, metes out his papal blessing. The fucker.' Alan corrected himself. 'At least he never met any lions.' Alan walked over a cobbled square in Trastevere. He looked in on a crib. Italian cribs were more exotic than Irish cribs, gold tinselled wise kings looking on the red lit infant like voyeurs, the exhalation of incense from the straw. Walking through Rome, Alan saw most vividly, for the first time in years, the face of Eileen Carmody. This time he did not see her in reference to history, but as an Irish girl who had reached out for love and been rejected.

Christmas morning 1950, Pope Pius XII made a sermon, exhorting a greater volume of prayer to Mary. That very year he'd ordained that Our Lady had been assumed into Heaven. On his way to the Irish College, Alan thought of a statue of Mary in the bogs near Athlone, her cloak mildewed, her eyes blackened, but her secret the secret of Ireland, despite weather and historical outrage – survival.

Father Anthony welcomed him with a cold white double handclasp. Alan was wearing his best, a tie, a suit. He was ushered in. They had port together under a portrait of a consummate cardinal. Father Anthony saw his brothers racing onto a radiant field in a pre-Christmas dinner hurling match. He imagined Christmas dinner, a big basted Mayo turkey, Limerick ham, boiled in watercress, shreds of it still clinging, brussels sprouts, roast potatoes. The smell wafted to Rome. The door was opened and Alan brought to the banquet. The table was most noticeably laden with green grapes. Everything was going smoothly – talk of Irish battles, Benburb, Scarrifhollis, Aughrim – until a fat nun walked in bearing a turkey and recognised Alan from an Irish newspaper as someone missing from Athlone. He was brought back to Ireland a few days later in a straitjacket, the nuns from Mayo, the nuns from Roscommon, the nuns from Armagh pouring through his head in the plane. He spent a few years going in and out of mental hospitals. He resumed his job as a National teacher. His tales of Cromwell no longer had the glitter. After a few years I no longer see Alan Mulvanney – he faded out of a portrait of a young man.

On leaving Ireland in January 1944 my mother, Eileen Carmody, felt she had taken an overdose of swan's meat. It stuck in her belly. Going between Ireland and England during the war you felt any moment you could be sunk. Women prayed against the slitting of the Liverpool dawn. In London, like her mother, she got a job with the nuns. She had an address bundled in her hand. The war had produced a new breed of tramps, men and women who went around muttering evangelical sayings to themselves. There was something disused about Eileen. She wore blue. Light broke through huge windows, shining on the floor. There was always a distance, even a sliver of a distance between her and her mop. Nuns swam into the shadows. Sometimes a prayer rose from her as she leaned on the mop. 'Dear God, take me back to innocence, holy purity. Make me happy again.' But happy she couldn't be. She was estranged from happiness. London was a surfeit. She walked the streets, people drifting like soot. In Leicester Square she saw a child in a blue coat who reminded her of Alan. In March, however it happened, she changed jobs, going to work in a hotel in Tavistock Square. There she wore blue again and behaved with equal vacuity as she cleaned floors. One day a man came from behind, an assistant in the hotel, placing his hands on her breasts. In a storeroom he seduced her, calling her Molly Malone and his Connemara colleen. After that she gave herself to him, over and over again. It had been so long since she'd slept with anyone that when it came, sex, it was like a drug. She went from one sex act to another. Men raced across the sands of Normandy, a hallucinatory whiteness about the sands. With an Irish girl called Teresa Mulcahy, Eileen got the train north. Both girls wore mauve chiffon scarves that day. Teresa was from Mullingar, she'd worked in the hotel with Eileen but in her home town of drowsy tobacco signs practised as a prostitute. Leeds gave them a home, it gave them a trade. They both worked as prostitutes in a brothel in a dingy back street there. For a while Eileen dyed her hair red and curled it even more ravenously. Teresa Mulcahy sang 'The Boys from the County Armagh' late at night. Men walked by in the blackened streets outside. A streak went through a window. Eileen felt a weight like a sinking ship.

Letters arrived from Ireland, dull stamps on them, gossip about geese and clouds. Eileen slept with an American G.I. one night who spoke of the beauty of Oregon, the sea, the cormorants, the whales going south in winter. Bombs exploded in Dresden: men, women, children a myriad florets of fire. Eileen moved again, this time to

Newcastle where she undertook her trade more selectively, wearing black, a prostitute in a house near the docks. The war came to an end. The king and queen waved to admiring crowds from the balcony of Buckingham Palace. Eileen privately addressed the British Empire. 'You came and took us over and drove us out. Will we always be a nation of wanderers because of you? Will there ever be a home we can feel safe in?' Then one day whe met my father.

Thomas Hitchens was born of lowly farming stock in Northumberland in 1898. He had two brothers and one sister. His family owned one cow. When Thomas was very small his father went to war – to the Boer War and much later to the First World War. Christ was Christ of the resurrection in their home and war a symbol of the resurrection. Thomas's mother would look into the sunshine outside as though Christ would rise like a trampoline artiste in a visiting circus bearing tidings of her husband. When he was of age, Thomas went to war himself, to India. For over twenty years he became a photograph, an incandescence in his eyes, a perplexity with images of cows ploughing sacred patterns beside the Ganges, of little boys with rump legs practically levitating over that river, of pacifist revolutionaries beside it, soporifically weaving ancestral memories of young English preachers with red scarves in Galway city in the 1630s preaching love, brotherhood and the renunciation of arms. There was little talk of the renunciation of arms in military barracks in India. A young soldier grew old, losing his hair. Thomas was sent back to Europe, landed like a gift in Normandy, forged east until he encountered faces emerging like wraiths from concentration camps, their eyes the eyes of the dead Arms aloft of their own accord. He returned to the north of England, a fall out of prosperity assailing you in the air, factories, suburban houses burgeoning under your feet; got a job in a brother's newly opened factory in Newcastle, quickly rose to prominence, crushing a scarlet handkerchief in the breast pocket of a heavily lined suit, met my mother. She made love like no one else, a blind thing rising for air, sweat slithering off her, her breasts coiled between you, the force of her embrace making you forget war, massacres, young British soldiers doing the foxtrot in women's clothes in military barracks in India on New Year's Eve. There was the memory of war, of famine, an absorption of rocks in her. He fell in love with her.

She married in a white dress, her eyes black as bog water, raven hair rivetingly curled, her figure standing in the middle of a room, fingers curled about anemones, her beauty a moat. No one dared ask questions. He'd always see her as a gull which had strayed into an alien hemisphere. And one day she was pregnant with me.

During her pregnancy she was often suddenly called by some memory into the suburban Newcastle sunset, Alan, a novel in a drawer. What had gripped her most about that novel was not a young man and a young woman on the same white horse preaching peace in Ireland in the 1640s but Cromwellian soldiers, garbed in red, stamping the harvest fields, beating drums to warn the native Irish to be gone over the Shannon by the following spring. She saw them coming, a misplaced people, laden with geese and cattle. She stood among the rocks again, her country, and watched them converge, red faces, bloodied eyes, the weight of a Gaelic dictum hanging over them, 'A people is stronger than a lord', and felt the outrage and passed that outrage on to me.

[8]

The king has been a poor prisoner
A prisoner long in Spain.
And Willie of the Winsbury
Has lain long with his daughter at home.

What ails thee now my daughter Janet?
You look so pale and wan.
Have you any sore sickness
Or yet been lying with a man?

I have gotten no sore sickness
Nor yet been lying with a man.
But it is for you my father dear
So long been over in Spain.

Take off, take off your berry brown gown
Stand naked on a stone
That I might see you by your shape
Whether you be a maiden or none.

When I was very young I heard a folk song in Northumberland that stayed with me, about a king who returns from captivity to find his daughter has slept with someone. When he discovers it's not a knight or a nobleman he ordains the death of the culprit until he comes face to face with him and finds that his beauty is such that he too would have slept with him had he been a woman. Northumberland was a primal place for me, childhood visits to a farmhouse, a portrait of my father in military uniform on an oak cupboard.

When I was five my parents moved to Leeds, my father being made manager of a factory there. We lived in a suburban house at the end of a hill, a red letter-box outside.

My mother had found herself as unaccepted in England as in Ireland, so times she wasn't drinking gin in bars with her husband she was at home sitting in black.

When the other children were still wearing Davy Crockett outfits miraculously I became a teddyboy. I don't know how it happened, red jacket, immaculate white shirt, black skeleton trousers, but I stood on rubbish mounds, surveying the moors, breeze furrowing through the purples and pinks of the heather. I took to puffing on a cigarette at an early age. I observed. I was the outsider, intruder.

I'd never been baptised. My mother had either omitted to do so or hadn't had it done by design. There were no signs of religion in our home. But there was a sense of something outside the door other than boys in Davy Crockett outfits.

These things came to a head when my grandmother arrived from Ireland shortly after my ninth birthday, a crotchety lady in black, she outdid herself in black witch's boots. Very soon we formed an alliance against my mother's silence and my father's distance – a frail, fast walking Irish woman and an English teddyboy wandering about Leeds, standing together over a spot where broken glass had been merged by generations of feet into flat diamonds, visiting pubs, talking to alcoholic priests and debauched ex-nuns, pictures of virginal kneed hurlers on the wall. In these pubs, singers singing Irish songs, feet tapping to jigs, I saw my first vision of Irish manhood, young labourers, their coal black hair, their pale frail faces building into a picture of a person at the back of my mother's mind, whom she sometimes mentioned, Alan Mulvanney.

I walked into a room one day and there she was naked. She turned to me, a teddyboy, not ashamed. She was sitting in front of a mirror. I saw by her eyes that she was thinking of him again, whoever he was, and I slipped away, back to the rubbish dumps from where I could see horizon smoke and distant heather.

My grandmother had her store of stories: the day Father O'Mahony was shot by the Tans, his bleeding face falling into a jar of honey; the day the lady of the manor was held up at gunpoint by the 'lads' as she cycled, strawberries robbed from her basket. In turn my mother took up the stream of stories and told us the tale of *A Cavalier Against Time*, a magical tale spun by a boy she'd known once. There was a fire in our house in Leeds. It blazed as she told us about swans and cavaliers. She was falling in love again, a young man and a young woman traversing the bogs of Ireland on a white horse. That Christmas she bought two dozen John McCormack records, John McCormack rumbled onto a street where little cowboys fired guns.

Down by the salley gardens my love and I did meet;
She passed the salley gardens with little snow-white feet.
She bid me take love easy, as the leaves grow on the tree;
But I, being young and foolish, with her would not agree.

For the first time I became curious. There was a country beyond a suburban street in Leeds at the end of the fifties.

Where did this country lie? Was it geographical or an historical invention? My mother was good at stories and therefore I invented it: a picture of a Protestant bishop with a fat belly in gold, two boys, their hair fair, their eyes pink, a girl, a silver bodkin in her red hair, her cloak emerald, a young man called a cavalier because of his red trousers, all standing in a neglected corner of Ireland, preaching peace. My mother spoke of Ireland more insistently. She was thinking of going back, what to do I don't know. She walked streets in Leeds with more of a sense of inspiration. A world opened before her eyes – an Irish street full of young men with white shirts, braces, hands in their pockets. Maybe she'd go back for a while and plant sweetpeas in the garden of the lodge house which had long been neglected and locked up. My father at first didn't listen to her, but one day he wrote to a factory which was just about to be opened in my mother's home town and he got a job in it as manager. We weren't due to leave before Easter 1962. In the meantime I was sent to a grammar school where I had to shed my teddyboy apparel. English boys, for some reason picking out the Irishness in me, aimed paper darts at me, buffeted me with foul farts from fat bottoms in the showers. In class I stared stoically at a map of the world pin-pointing all the places disturbed by the British empire. At Christmas I donned my teddyboy outfit again, brought a chubby girl guide to a Methodist hall where I danced until they were all forgotten, the fat English boys, the paper darts, the farts, the graffiti of the British empire on the map on the wall. Later I took her home and kissed her on a moonlit night in an avenue in Leeds.

We left, Easter 1962. Our house was sold. We were moving into the lodge house in County Galway. My father had gone before us. The factory was opened, a bucket of holy water thrown on it by a bishop, if you were to believe him. Before I left I said goodbye to the hills, the lavatories, pictorials on them which told you a lot about perverse love, the smoke, the old men fading into the factory smoke, an English childhood, silent streets where little cowboys roamed and an emptiness descended that tore you inside and drove you off looking for colour and excitement.

On the plane from Manchester to Dublin my mother spoke to a woman in a brown suit from Limerick, a brown hat on her head, a cameo of Robert Emmet on her blue brooch, who'd been seeking her eighteen-year-old son run away with a coloured doctor's wife from her city. She hadn't succeeded in finding him. But landing at Dublin airport she said, 'Blessed be the will of God.' A train tugged west. Frothy white blossom was coming to Ircland. I saw a young man and a young woman riding through the white blossom. It was another time, blossoming at a time of war.

[9]

A street came to life, one by one the shops rouge and mustard fronted. Eileen Carmody had returned a respectable woman, wife of the factory manager and all, but people still shunned her. Women looked a little reservedly at her in the hotel. She was still the prostitute. She was still the one who gave her mother-of-pearl, eighteen-year-old body to big fleshy men. She had this dignity at least. She'd gone to Athlone in a liquorice black coat to meet a young man once and she'd gone out with him, walking a street with a dash of red light.

It was the stone walled fields which first shocked me, converging in waves on the town. I walked the street, lit up in my red jacket, singled out. Eyes stared carnivorously. I longed for the green lush hills of Northumberland. I longed for the blue sea of Northumberland. Here I was adrift. My mother took the initial shock of non-acceptance with bravery. As summer came she wore a white summer dress and like a dove led me through the old spots of town.

This had been a garrison town. It boasted a main street replenished with limestone houses. Here a Russian woman who threw wine parties and who'd drowned herself had lived. Near this house was a

35

men's club full of photographs of young soldiers blown apart in the First World War. Country women came to and went from the big grocery shops. Trees touched the street and blew it alive. Beyond it a river. Beyond it in another direction a demesne. Some people remembered the last of the ladies of the house going to church in carriages, meringue hair rolled under the canopy of their hats, a pile of berries on their mauve hats, and orange chrysanthemums surrounding them in the carriage in autumn. Here some dachshunds were buried. Over their grave an epitaph, 'Vanity of vanities, saith the preacher, vanity of vanities; all is vanity.'

It's funny now in a military barracks in Belfast, writing this, crossing out, patching together, trying to evoke, failing, doodles, portraits of nude women on the wall. Outside orange lights like diseased mushrooms. Inside silence, a desk, a volume of Keats, diverse pages. This is something that I've always wanted to do, go back, and now that I'm leaving, white shirts with bone white collars, a few short-sleeved Fair Isle jerseys, a few pairs of jeans packed, I do it. But it's so painful. It's like putting down a world except that world is continually falling apart by the force of a nuclear bomb.

Spring came to the town, early summer, laburnum, red hawthorn. My mother's hair rushed out, black. I walked with her by the river, in the demesne of the house. Tiger-lilies burnt outside our house. Sometimes I just sat in the café, watching straw shift outside, an old man going by in a cart full of turf, the grass falling to one side on the fair Green. Then one morning, my mother behind me, I saw them going to the old house, a group of children holding bushels of flowers, missals, rosaries, led by an older boy, his hair orange, his T-shirt mustard, his face covered by a bucketful of freckles, a girl beside him, she too in command, her hair very black, her skin pale, her manner determined.

[10]

Eugene McDermott lived in a house at the end of the main street. His father owned a hardware store. To one side was a faded advertisement for liners from Cobh to New York. Eugene's father came from East Galway, hurling people, thick kneed people. His mother was of a farming family in the Midlands. She grew up beside the Shannon, a

36

girl in a white dress with other sisters in white dresses walking among the yellow cabbage seed which grew in profusion. Each of these sisters, seven in all, had been blown away by tuberculosis. The most strange and mysterious case among these farming people, though, was a brother, already balding, who'd run away to England, joined the Merchant Navy, was bombed during the war, survived in the water for forty-eight hours, died of unknown circumstances in a London bed-and-breakfast house after the war, a red-haired girlfriend beside him. Eugene's grandfather had gone there, found his son dying, afterwards walked London streets, the whine of a Byzantine rite issuing from a Greek Orthodox church, the old man falling on his knees, the whine taking all, chocolate papers and bundled trips to the Eucharistic Congress in 1933.

As a small child Eugene visited parts of Ireland in which he was aware of his mother cycling with her other sisters once, beside rivers in autumn, swans on the rivers, over bridges, the girls arriving at a farmhouse, the heads of mares sticking over fences in the buoyant sunshine, the smell of newly churned butter and gladiatorial mice greeting the girls as they entered the farm kitchen. Eugene as a small child also stood on station platforms, purple lilac falling onto brown rusted bridges, where he felt his mother to have stood with those sisters before they passed into heaven. He waited in cemeteries in hilly parts of the Midlands with his mother as she stood above graves, glass domes with red plastic flowers in them reflecting her. He wanted to hold his mother back from grief, but there was no way. He wanted to tug her away, but she spoke her prayers ardently now. Trains went by outside. A river cut through fields of stone walls. Eugene had one older sister, a civil servant in Dublin. He contented himself with escaping. He met Cherine Finnerty to escape.

[11]

A little black-haired girl, Cherine Finnerty had her roots in the tinkers on both sides of her family. Her people had been uprooted in Cromwell's time and had travelled the roads since; so her father, guardian of the local cemetery, liked to think. He had fanciful stories: the time his ancestors all took to the highways in the eighteenth century and robbed noblemen; the time they'd sailed to a remote west of Ireland island during the Famine in the nineteenth century and survived on roasted whiting. Cherine had grown up listening to the soporific blur of her father's stories. Outside was the cemetery; aria singing spinsters who'd thrown themselves from windows on the main street were buried there, dwarfs who'd ranted about the civil war. When Cherine was nine, her mother, a black-haired McDonagh, had walked into the river holding a rosary. Cherine and her father were looked after now by a deaf and dumb sister. Apart from her, Cherine had many brothers and sisters who were scattered, mainly around England. One brother drove a ramshackle van the length and breadth of Ireland, selling religious *objets d'art*, taking Cherine once, a girl in a worn strawberry cardigan, to a promontory in West Kerry where pilgrims bowed over softened stone; the little girl standing on the promontory, the skies opening on her, her cheeks peach from the rain, feeling the isolation and yet the determination of her ancestry, tinkers converging on the western bays of Ireland. Recently her brother had been brought to court for interfering with little children, but by far the most famous and the most prestigious of her relatives was a cousin who'd gone to Hollywood and starred in a film as a leprechaun in a green outfit. She had come back once or twice, running her blue poodle across the bogs, throwing her delicate arms in the air. Then she'd written, describing her affair with Montgomery Clift, describing him, tormented forehead, black, lazy quiff, hands in his pockets, telling of trips they'd taken by Big Sur, of lobster they'd eaten, luscious red lobster against azure panoramas of the Pacific. Then it had failed, the affair, her career. The postcards stopped, the letters. Some local lads muttered that they'd seen her riding naked on a pig's back in a blue movie in Manhattan. Truth was she was most likely walking a deflated poodle on the promenade of Malibu Beach, herself in a long dilapidated coat, her early fifties hair-style still intact. Cherine treasured these precocious memories by putting Hollywood ikons in a collage on the wall next to the cemetery: her aunt, Montgomery Clift, most of all Montgomery Clift, Montgomery Clift all over the place. Of all tragedies in a mainly tragic family this was the greatest of tragedies, a relative fallen from grace. Cherine escaped from the burden of it by summoning the local children to the Green – tramps eyeing them suspiciously, Guinness bottles in their pockets – and leading them forward to search for ghosts.

A most terrible thing happened early in August. Marilyn Monroe killed herself in Hollywood. As Cherine was the one closest to Hollywood she made a speech on the veranda of the manor house, now a boys' school, where they'd gone looking for ghosts.

'The good always die young,' she declared. 'They give us their gifts and we throw tin cans in their faces.' Her ribbon stood up against the light, a swarm of blue dots on white. 'Marilyn Monroe has died among the purple bed sheets of Hollywood.' With that statement she took herself to a point between cypresses planted by a lady of the house who'd visited Italy the year Keats had died, urns commemorating a Victorian music hall artiste who'd married a lord of the manor on either side of the little girl, her face numbly wedged in her hands.

There was silent consternation among the children until Eugene McDermott edged forward, took his place beside Cherine and comforted her in the sun.

In a way the death of Marilyn Monroe was a relief. For years Cherine had been promising a ghost. No ghost had been forthcoming. This year she asserted that a young rake of the house, who'd once beaten on a pie-bald mare called Sally over the pot-holed Midland roads of Ireland to Dublin, partaking in fiendish rites in the Hell-Fire Club overlooking the city, would make an appearance at the end of August. The middle-class children of the town, who mainly comprised her retinue, tolerated Cherine only for entertainment. Now that the entertainment was flagging they were bordering on a revolt.

At moments of less pressure Cherine would seat herself by the lily pond with Eugene, he in short trousers, orange lily heads bobbing over the white petals, and discuss her future plans. She hoped to go to Hollywood and make a film about the life of her illustrious relative, Sabina Finnerty.

Funeral cars dragged through the summer, laden with red carnations. Poppies were wreathed into the fields, each one a memorial for Marilyn. A cloud shadow surprised a field of corn, still lime. A group of boys, in blue and white striped T-shirts, breakfast honey still cascading around their mouths, lined up as if they were going to pick up stones and throw them at Cherine. Then one morning she pointed in triumph, 'That's him.' Between the urns, overlooking the fields, stood a young aristocrat in a red jacket, white immaculate shirt, black skeleton trousers, hands in his trousers' pockets, his dark hair edged into a quiff and his eyes honest and blue. The children were overtaken by amazement, until Tommy Morahan, the grocer and vintner's son, shouted, 'That's the Hitchens' boy.'

Years later, I could see that, for those magical moments of silence, the distance of green scintillating grass between us, I entered their world, Eugene's and Cherine's, without a childhood and they entered mine with childhoods but desperately wanting to shed them. But now in a Belfast military barracks I, Sergeant Jeremy Hitchens, can see I went much further. I travelled beyond their world, their innocence, Eugene's and Cherine's, until I saw him, more clearly than before, Alan Mulvanney, that unwreathed laureate of Ireland, his black hair, white shirt, hands in his trousers' pockets, his world, his innocence, and I felt the tremors – a young man having a glass of red wine with a young woman in Galway city in the seventeenth century – but inherited this, a chaos which will go on and on, which nothing will stop, neither journeys nor movement, nor changes of role, nothing except a gesture of love.

Adolescence

Young girls cover the bodies of the dead in linen at night in Galway city. Lachrymose prayers rise from the people of Galway ensconced on the hills round about to avoid the plague. A cardinal in red sails out, cursing the Blakes of Galway. Images from Alan's novel. A young man in a portrait holding a gold medallion. That summer's day, walking home part of the way with Eugene and Cherine, fluff streaming in the air, I didn't listen to their conversation but considered Alan, his search for innocence, for childhood.

Cherine Finnerty failed to turn up at school that autumn. She started working, two days a week with the nuns, two days a week in the ice-cream shop cum florist's at the end of the street. She took to shrouding her curls in a scarf. I often sat with her in the café, dark clouds piled up over the darkened thoroughfare outside on which lord deputies once dragged by on mules' backs on their way from Dublin to Galway. Every flick of a cigarette end, my pale hand edged by a pink cuff, every tipping of a Coca Cola bottle was an encounter again with that novel. One day on the prom by the river at the back of the church, I told its story to Eugene, long fawn trousers now complementing his auburn hair and his fawn jersey rimmed by darker brown patterns, and to Cherine. Not even Cherine, plummeting among books in the library, could find imagery which caught her imagination so much, a young Irishman wavering among the army fires of Europe in pursuit of his lover. During the Cuban crisis, Cherine, on the prom, in a scarf and coat, under a tree whipped bare of leaves, confessed to Eugene and myself, the three of us standing, that she hoped there'd be a war. That comment seems odd now in the middle of a real if secretive war, bodies in the sewers outside, wounds in the heart, a militia of ghosts in the night. But the distance between Belfast now and a small town in the sixties doesn't seem too far, the same statue of Mary dominating both places, the young I.R.A. dead dedicated to her here, incantations to her invoked in newspapers which ultimately immerse fish and chips on the Falls Road, in the small town her statue overlooking broken Coca Cola bottles in a backyard just off the main street. I spent a lot of time on that main street in my first few years in the small town, standing in my red jacket outside the chip shop, waiting for the first neon of evening. The Irish education system being as it was, I had to pass two years in National school before graduating to the priest organized boys' secondary school. In the meantime I had to undergo a year in the notorious Mr. Hearne's class in seventh grade at National School.

The year began peaceably. I visited the opening of the October fair with my mother. In a long-sleeved white shirt, my thumbs in my trousers' pockets, I confronted her. Mellow light fell in bucketfuls on pie-bald ponies. She was in a blue sleeveless summer dress. Behind her I could see another young man in another time who was also dressed in a white shirt but with sky-blue braces. I smiled at him and he smiled back.

Mr. Hearne's classroom was full of photographs of the heroes of 1916, one woman's photograph among them, that of a widow of one of the men of 1916. She had left her child in a pram on a beach after her husband's execution and walked to her own death into the Irish Sea. Her dress was white, her hair in a bun on top of her head, the beginning of a smile almost vanquished by a high, vanilla, afternoon, sea-side sun. Her presence in the classroom was comforting. Mr Hearne emerged from these tableaux, his face a conflagration of scorched reds and purples, his hair a wistful silver, the whites of his eyes livid as his hands dug into his jacket pockets.

Tobias Hearne was born in a town in County Tipperary sometime in 1900. His father owned a big store, lemon fronted. Women in black crowded in from the country to this store, tinkers left their carts for it, big bulwarks of men drew on clay pipes outside it. There was agitation and prosperity in this town, many skulls of green cabbages outside the store of Tobias' father, water gurgling from a Neptune's mouth above a font in the square. You bought tickets to America in the store, fresh greens. It was the dominant store of this proud housed town. Mrs. Hearne trailed her offspring into the countryside of buttercups and falling stone walls. She had sad eyes like many women of her time. She considered the rosary or the battles of the Irish Brigade long ago. One of her ancestors had fought for the Hungarian Hussars. Maybe it was because of this – priests coming from the Continent, plunging into yellow ochre sofas, speaking of the Hussars – maybe because of the times that were in it, Redmond bawling in Dublin and Fenians floating in every disguise in the market squares and the ports of Ireland, but young Tobias Hearne, a lanky lad, took a more than keen interest in history at the local Christian Brothers'. He paused over his brown desk and his eyes summoned up a battle in the days of the Fianna and more recently the Manchester martyrs, young Irishmen wronged once again, this time in England, for seeking to readjust the fate of Ireland, to mend the veil which hid the hermetic face of Mother Ireland. He was, as it happened, the Christian Brothers' favourite pupil and that was no mean achievement. Chariots were riding forth to avenge Mother Ireland alias Cathleen ni Houlihan. Excitement ran in undercurrents in the market square. It posited stillness on people. 1916 came and went. Christian Brothers stopped talking. They just stood in the darkness of the classroom as if their tremulous waiting would help. Mrs. Hearne took to fits of crying. No one knew why she cried. She cried on the living room sofa. She saw battles and slayings long ago. Tobias Hearne left County Tipperary in a long coat on an autumn day, heading to Dublin to study as a National teacher. On the platform was an advertisement for Monte Carlo. A woman procured a cigarette in a long holder in the poster. Head bent Tobias Hearne caught the train.

Dublin then had fangs of violence; violence, smoke spat from unexpected quarters. Tobias Hearne continued to pursue a knowledge of history and perfect the images he already had. There was blood in the water of this city, in the pools. One day a little girl was killed in a sex murder by the Dodder and her body found, lying in a pool of water, her face, messed up with blood, staring upwards. She got little attention. Women huddled together in twosomes by College Green. Who would prevail in this fight? And the fight seemed to be between good and evil. These forces floated in the air in Dublin, puffed in the breeze. Tobias Hearne cycled west in the summer. He and fellow students took the train to Galway, wheeled their bicycles off, ladies in red petticoats pulling their black shawls around them outside the Great Southern Hotel, vegetables sprawled out for purchase on the limestone roadsides, and they mounted their bicycles, eyes and hardy bodies set in the direction of the coast, male legs entwined with hair rotating with calm. The west was full of blue bays then. They'd gone to polish up their Irish phrases, of course, and their use of Irish. They were dedicated to Irish. Maria Mulvanney. Eibhlin O'Rourke. They spun tales at night, young people lying on turf dusted floors, looking to the amethyst, downward slanting Atlantic sunsets, tales of Cúchulainn, Conor Mac Neasa, Ruairc Mac Suibhne. All the time, as the mythological heroes stepped forward and performed – like pantomime characters at the Queen's – woollen trousers, profusely and foolishly stockinged, they knew the history of Ireland was in the making. As melodion music sounded or feet tapped

45

on bare floors in dances, as sunsets burst orange, men were fighting, English against Irish, then Irish against Irish. The Irish won, then the Freestaters. On a tree lined street in Dublin in May, Tobias Hearne strolled into the National Library, opened a book on seventeenth-century Irish history, became preoccupied with the illustrations: Durer's Irish warriors there, one of them with his head inclined, almost penitentially; an Irish nobleman here, daintily treading in cloth shoes, hand outstretched; an Irish noblewoman somewhere else, enwrapped in a cloak, a solitary mountain, a wooden crucifix hanging above her breasts, and wrote on the back of his jotter, 'I want my life to be one of imparting a knowledge of Irish history to schoolchildren.'

The episode in Irish history which most obsessed him was the banishment to the west of the native Irish by Cromwell in 1653 and there was a poem written by a priest who made this journey which incorporated itself into Tobias' life and the lives of his friends because it commenced with a blessing. That blessing was employed on streets in Dublin under posters for the Royal as a kind of throwaway, mock-heroic au revoir.

> In the name of the Father full of virtue,
> in the name of the Son Who suffered pain,
> in the name of the Holy Ghost in power,
> Mary and her Son be with us.

Girls with cream skin in blue dresses hesitated for this blessing. Then it was ultimately invoked as a farewell when young students left Dublin to take up positions as teachers in diverse parts of the newly founded Irish Free State. Tobias Hearne left his digs in Rathmines, the environs of Rathmines, vegetable shops, newsagents which he'd often wandered around in a long coat, head down, considered the wrongs done to the Irish, considering history as it was made in this city, Robert Emmet's hanging in Thomas Street, his final heroic salute from the docks, and he took a train west on a day elm trees spiralled in Palmerston Park, the memory of Georgian squares, of Trinity cobbles painfully deserting his mind and the blues and reds of rhododendrons taking over, a young man's head rising from a dream to confront reality. He had come to a remote part of Ireland to teach history.

It was a little mound of a school he was accredited to, by a crossroads in dun countryside under a purple mountain. He had a small abode alongside it where he tended the brown carpets and buxom potted plants. There was one pinched stained glass window in this house. He'd stand outside at moments of light, passing greetings in Gaelic to slow and unadventurous passers-by. In the summer he'd be able to stand here all evening. Already there were suggestions of summer twilights, bodies of rouge over the lake. The wireless rumbled out news broadcasts in the evenings. Streams of cowslips trickled to him in little girls' cream fingers when it was spring. Eyes danced for Mr. Hearne, dainty lips radiated for him. The handsome, masculine school teacher stood above his goslings. Alone, he fingered a Victorian vase for frailty, he overlorded the demesne of a sitting room. Twilight smashed through. Hands in his jacket pockets he waited.

Now it happened that there was a sweetheart in Tobias Hearne's life. He'd known her from way back. She was one of a farming family in Tipperary. Her family lived beneath the genteel Galtee Mountains. When Tobias had been a year at the school she arrived. She came on the train, he met her at the station, the pony and trap carried them through the land of purple and red rhododendron bushes, of blushing mountain purples. The rhododendrons were exceedingly plush, especially so on an island in a small lake near the school house. Outside the school house he cloaked her in his arms. She wore a simple violet summer dress. She'd brought a cake in a lemon box. Her lips were curled with lipstick. 'Toby,' she said, 'I have to boil a few eggs for you.'

The marriage celebrations took place in the open air in Tipperary. Standing, he made a speech. Naturally it included history.

> In the name of the Father full of virtue,
> in the name of the Son Who suffered pain,
> in the name of the Holy Ghost in power,
> Mary and her Son be with us.

Why was it that at a feast by a long white, laid oak table under a blue mountain ridge that he saw mad people clasping the bars of a window in a mental hospital?

The little lair beside the school house provided a marital haven. Biscuits strayed in from Dublin, pink, fluffy marshmallows. Otherwise there were few intrusions from the outside world. Bars of chocolate breathlessly lay like emissaries, both a reassurance of what they had left and an affirmation of chosen solitariness. A clock slumbered, its paws outstretched. They tuned into news broadcasts together. Kevin O'Higgins was killed in Dublin. It was during Mrs.

Hearne's first pregnancy. Her knitting kneedles dug deeper into the socks she was knitting for the baby that was due. 'Sacred Heart of Jesus have mercy on his soul.' She checked her prayer, remembering that the sympathies of her husband, like those of most in Tipperary, were with the Republicans. She held her first child in her arms on the slope of green outside the house, looking to the valley below, in a blue summer dress, beaming. De Valera came to power, men who'd fought for the Free State marched in the new army, a double ardour in their eyes, the ardour of a cause confounded and that of a more mercenary position taken up. Photographs of children making their first holy communion sprung up like buttercups. There were many children. Neasa, Deirdre, Fachtna, the roll-call of Irish mythology. Little boys in cream vests and short baggy trousers confronted footballs. Jonquil hair was tremulously curled. An MG was bought and it brought the family to the sea. Mrs. Hearne lay in Tobias' arms. Her hair had grown longer. What should he call her? Deirdre, Maeve? The names of Irish heroines. A man from the government visited the valley to open a forestry plantation, standing in front of an open car. 'He's got a nose like Mr. Hitler's,' a scarved woman was heard to whisper. A shadow simultaneously skimmed the valley. Before you could catch your breath narrow rains sheathed fledgling trees. 'Cúchulainn walked by the beach below the hill of Slaney.' Mrs. Hearne was reading from a book of Irish mythology one winter's evening, babes on her lap, little ones by her feet, peeping into the expansive pages with scarlet and Lincoln green illustrations, the more mature ones vigilantly standing by the trojan arms of the armchair in warm and generously patterned short-sleeved jerseys, other little ones in their father's arms, when a man burst in. Someone nostalgic for battle had blown up the local garda station. The news of Mr. Hearne's transfer came in autumn. Children snuggled in the gold outside when it arrived. Marigolds bathed in gold light in a white, cerise ornamented bowl on the kitchen larder inside, flecks of dust swimming uncertainly about it. Mr. Hearne's voice could sonorously be heard through the half open kitchen window dictating the facts of history to the interested members of his family. 'This is the time O'Neill and O'Donnell went to Italy, the time Cromwellian soldiers, in red coats, stalked the harvest fields, beating drums to warn the native Irish to be gone over the Shannon by the following spring.' The kitchen clock croaked. Standing, Mrs. Hearne accepted the letter outside the house from the postman. Afterwards she approached the marigolds in the kitchen quizzingly, her face, confused, breathing upon their phosphorescence. They did not leave for many months. A pony and trap

48

brought them to the station through the luminous rhododendrons. On the road behind, Mr. Hearne saw, or thought he saw, a little girl with buttermilk hair crying.

It was difficult to forget young men in coats too long for them treading avenues in Dublin under green, piled up leaves on golden evenings, but gradually the footsteps receded. A young man turned a corner and other footsteps took over, the crunch of Blueshirts' heels, the more shadowy treading of boy scouts at a Corpus Christi procession, an Irish flag flying, green, gold with starched white in the middle, and the Vatican flag, gold and white. The town Mr. Hearne found himself in boasted a mental hospital, a river, a main street. He and his family were ensconced in a small, threatening suburban-type bungalow with neat hedges outside. You could see the neighbours go by, a Protestant lady who looked as if she'd received a battering. Mr. Hearne was at his height of handsomeness, hair neatly parted on the left. He played hockey with the local team. On the mental hospital grounds his stick reached for a ball. But something arrested his movement. He confronted a classroom of emaciated boys – it was an all-boys national school he was teaching in – but he could no longer see the Irish being driven west before Cromwell's men but more contemporary images. For more than twenty years he stared at a classroom of boys and as he lectured on history saw history as it was happening before his eyes: a frog-like Vatican emissary poises his hand to be kissed by an Irish politician; bare, skeleton armed young men spike fields about the river against German invasion; a flood of bishops overruns the map of the twenty-six counties, the verbal mouths of Irish politicians straining to kiss their fingers; a young politician battles with bishops and is overcome; helicopters land; factories sprout up; politicians rush from the helicopters; the map of Ireland is bathed in holy water and pound notes; and in the midst of this mayhem something crashed in Mr. Hearne. His hair blanched, his face became purple and red, and the whites of his eyes shot out. He swept before bishops' rings himself. He punished children for not being of the right class background. He became a torment to his own family. Sometimes, glowering at a class from the throbbing corner of his eye or by the draconian Treaty Stone outside King John's castle in Limerick during an educational tour, they came to him for no reason, illustrations seen on a leafy May evening in the National Library in a book about seventeenth-century Ireland, lords, noble ladies, their dresses dripping, an Irish chieftain, a wolfskin hugged around him, his crafty eyes glinting and a black fountain of a moustache sliming about his mouth, none of them saying anything, all of them standing still, a dumb travelling show, yet a question in their eyes, a response.

Mr. Hearne raged. He raged about the forcible exit of the O'Sullivans from West Cork in the latter part of the sixteenth century, about the Cromwellian sacking of Drogheda, about the ships which issued in multitudes from the ports of Ireland during the Famine, bodies prostrate on the decks under the Atlantic light, their faces looking up. He raged so much he failed to notice for a while I was one of them, a Cromwellian. When he did he raged against me too. He had me shed my red jacket and wear blue. He stood on my black, patented shoes, stared into my eyes, his spittle landing on my face. The only thing he perceived in those eyes though was the storm clouds of humiliation, pink ignitions on white. I tried desperately to hold back tears.

'There were woodcocks and partridges in Munster', he declared as if solely blaming me for their disappearance, 'before the British came.' As a little boy his parents would often bring him and his sister into the hills in the first automobile in town – an Austin Endcliffe – trundling along ribbony roads, settling in the hills over the Glen of Aherlow, the valley lush, honeyed below. Here Geoffrey Keating had hidden in his flight from the Lord President of Munster after the poet-priest had incurred the wrath of his would-be-lover Eleanor Laffan. The little boy would scramble through thickets with his sister, often stopping to pick up an acorn, an arch of a twig, sensing something, another civilization, looking up, as thrushes brushed through the light, to see monks chanting and ladies in saffron roaming. Now he looked through the same passage of light and saw only me, an English boy, an alien.

My mother became more forlorn, face in her hands by a fire in a darkened kitchen, often a black sleeveless crinoline evening dress on her for no reason, her arms vulnerable and talcumed. My father, despairing of his burden of Ireland, stayed on late in his office, poring over the contents of profoundly weighty ledgers, silver spectacles on the edge of his honed nose. Granny, distraught for exile and the anachronisms of exile afforded her, parked almost permanently on a tall stool above a straw strewn floor in a grocery cum bar on the main street, her blanched hand clasping a fulsome pint of Guinness, a skeletal silver ring about one of the fingers, a black hat pressing her down. I strolled to school, satchel wedged on my shoulder, a first fragment of snow dashed against a brown hair mat hung on a hedge to dry outside a tinker's caravan, disturbing in its flight the sleep of a rather vicious-looking tinker's dog.

As the year wore on Mr. Hearne's description of the sacking of Drogheda increased in impact and dementia. Little boys shivered like a bed of snowdrops. Again the flames shot up, the fires were reflected in the jewels bordering the dresses of ladies on their knees with their hands reaching out in vain pleading, swords gushed into pregnant wombs, scarlet cavalier cloaks managed elegantly to swish in the dusk and the church of Saint Peter was confounded in smoke and shrieks. Recovering from one of these deluges, Mr. Hearne turned his gaze towards the window one day the same moment as I did and our eyes briefly engaged along the way, but looking out the window our eyes saw different things. I saw Alan, a friend always gliding alongside me now, his version of history, his more tender tapestry of events.

Boys in blue and white striped jerseys overran the fair Green in a hurling match. Eugene, a sapling adolescent, shivered on the edge of the pitch, hands in his pockets. I would have approached him and asked him for companionship had it not been too cold.

At Christmas, just to show them, in blue, hands behind my back, dark hair, grown somewhat longer, carefully groomed, at the school concert, on a stage composed of four tables thrown together, I sang 'Mary's Boy Child' which my grandmother had taught me.

After Christmas I visited the convent crib with my mother. She looked at the child Jesus as if he was one of her own. Again it was 1943. A newsreel ran in her head, black and white. Children, hapless cases in their hands, rapidly converged on a train which was to bear them to a concentration camp. In Athlone a young man stood before the Infant, wondering how it was possible, birth in a world bordering on annihilation. A train crossed the bridge in Athlone, gold, and a young girl veered towards Athlone in a car, wondering whether she would be received into her lover's arms. Pink light flushed on my mother's black handbag now held in front of her with her two hands. Again a nun's tinsel star triumphed. The exhalation of straw swept around us. Standing alongside my mother, I ventured to approach Alan's question when the shared veneration of my mother and myself was shattered by the oncoming rattle of beads. We escaped.

Eugene sat in class, hands joined on the desk in front of him, a growing chestnut. Cherine, scarf on her head, mercilessly scoured books in the library, the librarian watching her from the sides of her eyes, wizened. Little old ladies in black crawled up the lane opposite. I wondered how I could get to know these people, Eugene and Cherine. What language did one use here? But my only reply was the articulation of neon on the main street as I huddled outside the chip shop at night in a grimy brown coat; little girls who worked in my

51

father's factory hunched alongside me, Pope John XXIII, an ermine collar around his neck, smiling benevolently above the spectacle of bubbling chips inside.

My mother grabbed her scarf and headed off on the Galway road one day in March. Of late she'd been overwhelmed by restlessness. She'd returned to this country – for what? To decipher a shred of integrity in her own experience. And what had she been rewarded with? Endless languishment in a darkened kitchen. A fleet of clouds soared over, Armada ships. Of late they'd been haranguing her again, the Micks, the Micheáls, the Michaels, but different ones, less gaunt, brown scapulars not necessarily dangling on the cream billows of their chests. 'Sacred Heart of Jesus. Sweet Mary.' As a prostitute in the north of England she'd uttered aspirations – taught by black hooded, inquisitorial nuns at convent school – during sexual intercourse. She smiled. Perhaps she was a prostitute at heart. Long, wartime knickers, blue as Cadbury's chocolate covers dangled in front of her. A goose hesitated in its afternoon promenade to hiss in her direction. On the Galway road that March day Eileen Carmody encountered a young, half-idiot, farm labourer in a white shirt who grimaced in her direction. She led him by the hand to a dry spot in the bog and there, among the swaying blues and reds of the heather, had him make love to her, he on top of her. The liturgy gave way to imagery, currachs milled again to a place of pilgrimage in medieval Ireland.

That might have been it had there not been more . . . and more. A bare, skeleton bulb exploded in my father's office. He pretended not to hear the strings of rumour. Mr. Hearne looked at me, a new glee in his eye. Other centuries at last had come alive for him. My mother was Dervorgilla, Honora, Lady Kerry, Eleanor Laffan, one of the whores of Irish history.

My grandmother died in March. Her funeral was long and stringy – like herself. The night of her funeral it finally happened, an inner explosion long expected. From my vantage point outside the chip shop I flitted to Cherine's home by the cemetery. I was told she was not there. I turned on my heels and headed to Eugene's more regal home. The big, brown, oak, handsome door did not budge. On the white-washed side of the house a pictorial liner, already fading, bound from Cobh to New York sat in silent voyage. On the main street I began crying. A big, burly garda approached me and asked in a Kerry accent if I was Mr. Hitchens' son. He then proceeded to take my hand in his elephantine, hairy one and bring me home.

The following autumn, having started at the boys' secondary school – in a rare interim between rain – in my brown, greasy coat I led by the hand a thirteen-year-old girl, who worked in my father's factory, to a dry spot in the Blackwoods and there, a little old lady in black pushing a pram through the red berries nearby collecting firewood, laid the little girl on the ground, raising her antelope thighs, and made love to her. After that I led other young girls to the same spot and a similar fate. About the same time a girl who worked in my father's factory announced that she'd seen the Virgin Mary outside the factory. At the promptings of her young fellow workers a make-shift, chalk white, wafer-thin statue of Mary was hurriedly erected in the uncertain location of the apparition, an aureole of tangerine lights about her head at night. Shortly after that the young girl became pregnant and left for England. Boys with Elvis locks mourned. 'Our Lady of Coca Cola' I christened the statue, but 'Our Lady of Coca Cola' or not I went on, stalking a patch of light outside the chip shop, trying to string a small piece of life together, seeking more than anything to forget, the moments accumulating like pebbles on an island my grandmother had gone to to do penance, crawling on her bare knees over stones as rain trickled off the bald pates of old men.

[2]

'If I could I'd have given you summer '
It was a year after I'd started at the boys' secondary school. I stood at the kitchen door, unnoticed. My mother sat by the fire, face in her hands, the light not on. Tomorrow's cornflakes stood on top of the larder above her, further down a chocolate box cover surviving from the previous Christmas faced outward on a shelf, carefully fitted there by my mother, showing Golden Gate Bridge, San Francisco, lit up at night. I knew what my mother was thinking, that the gap between her and Alan was like that bridge, glamorously illumined, but always there. Myself I'd been out that night. I crouched at the door in my coat. I'd been brought by a girl to her home in the 'Terrace', the Calcutta of town, the two of us looking downward as we approached it, at the circles of rubble, the stalwart lying Guinness bottles, evangelical remarks bannered above us, advertisements for Guinness. I followed the girl upstairs as light fell on a blue Byzantine Mother and child. The girl's parents were away. She sat on a bed in her coat, shivering, hands in her pockets, behind her the Sacred Heart pointing

as usual in a demonstrative way to his bleeding heart, Elvis, his crotch about to rip. I sank into a chair. I knew what was expected of me, the requisite gesture, seduction, but this time I up and went, stealing away into the night. The night received me like an old friend, bog breezes, sweep of nettles, donkeys' brays. I walked and walked, past commanding church steeple, past river, past ballroom which housed orgies of lust and Country and Western bands. There was no dance tonight. Now I looked at my mother. I slipped away to my room. I began writing pornography that night. 'He stuck his...' But the images of bulging muscles, of syrupy biceps converted into different shapes. Mackerel boats glided over blue waters around Saint Macdara's Island. Baby seals were bludgeoned to death, their kindergarten voices crying out. An old man waited in a garden of orange trees and purple Judas trees for news from Ireland. On a black night during the school term I found myself rewriting Alan's novel.

[3]

The town where Martin Finnerty, Cherine's father, grew up, was created when tribes came together by a ford on a river, merging with their wares. Men on mules drew up on both sides of the ford in the distant dusk of history but one side was favoured more than the other. In later times Elizabeth built her fortress, now overgrown with ivy, on the other side of the ford. 'In olden times,' was Mr. Finnerty's way of describing it, 'In olden times men came on black mules with the colours of the four parts of Ireland, Connaught, Munster, Leinster or the red hand of Ulster and alighted, bargaining late into the night. Some waited in tents. Some set up homes here. So began our town.' 'Olden times', that was a favourite term of reference in the Finnerty household. It encapsulated a lot, times monks and nuns scurried about the district, demonstrating tall crosses with both hands, their mad, lit-up eyes looking up at the focal point of the crosses. The time a bishop had his crozier buried in a field by the river as he died in that place, his praying hands elevated in the air and his eyes on Heaven. In the nineteenth century, a parish priest found the crozier and threatened parishioners who failed to pay their dues with the issue of its spells. An elderly widow ran away with it, breaking it into little pieces, disseminating the pieces in a field of corn, again by the river.

The parish priest, gown-like, mildewed surplice on him, declared from the pulpit that the town would be cursed until the pieces came together again. 'Olden times' covered the whole range of things Gaelic in this area, the reigns of kings, the approach of chieftains across the low-lying misty terrain, the snorting of mares, everything up to the eventual takeover by the British when history became darker somehow, history became more intimate.

In the seventeenth century, a Royalist commander drank himself to death in an overshadowed house in the Blackwoods, his wife, the daughter of a Gaelic chieftain, stealing away with his money and her dowry, last seen in Galway city, tripping along Buttermilk Lane, lifting her scarlet dress from the mud, her money in a pouch, on her way to a waiting ship in the port which would take her to Europe. Years later after the Battle of Aughrim a Williamite soldier entered the house to find the skeleton still seated, a cobwebbed wine glass in the macabre fist and a sapphire ring on one of the outstretched fingers.

Towards the end of the same century a lady of the family who'd taken over the local estate after the Williamite triumph became fascinated with silver medieval Irish chalices, usually, added Mr. Finnerty, winking his eye to direct your attention to her motives, studded with jewels. There was a portrait of this woman in the boys' secondary school, her mansion, which showed a hooded figure on a bridge accepting a chalice from a peasant with waves of mountains in the background.

Some bloody eigit of a painter in England thought there were mountains in the town! The penal times were slumberous around this town, a nation slept. The black bogs sheltered silver chalices the lean and hen-like hand of that lady had not gotten upon. Daniel O'Connell's voice echoed from the four corners of Ireland here; the 'uncrowned king of Ireland' never paid the town a visit. It had to be conceded, however, that it was the Famine which made most mark here and in evidence of this a rat-grey great workhouse still stood, burnt to a shell but its eyes staring out, 'the skull of Queen Victoria' someone called it. Peasants wheeled the corpses of their relatives in to the main street like sacks of oatmeal, coming and going with them as in a market of death, adolescent girls, pubescent boys laid out. You could stroke these corpses sometimes, so real were the pictures Martin Finnerty painted of them, boys with straw hair, girls, hands folded on their wan tummies. 'There'd be fights and brawls in the workhouse even in the midst of dying,' Martin declared, 'ould women fighting over a morsel of bread.'

Cherine, a child, saw one particular woman, a witch, gloating over

55

a crust of bread held on a tin tray by a Quaker before grabbing it. Near the town was a mound on which skulls accumulated, grinning skulls, melancholic skulls. A priest had a cabin of a church erected on the spot, a stained glass window inside showing a girl in an emerald skirt and brown shawl reaching for bread. Martin Finnerty, a chubby child with a prong of black, curly hair on his forehead and a pouting mouth sipped nettle soup in the darkened kitchen of his Flea Lane home to the sound of the rattle of guns outside, firstly to the guns of the Irish fighting the British and the British fighting the Irish, secondly to the guns of the Irish fighting the Irish, lastly to the ghost of the rattle of guns. Flea Lane was so called because here the riff-raff lived, according to the middle-class people of town – the women in shining, black satin dresses with cotton wool hair, ruddied parchment of skin and always anxiety in their eyes, the bank clerks on giddy bicycles, the shop keepers with bowler hats pulled down over their heads and walking sticks prodding the limestone pavements in front of them – or the 'scruff' as one bilious woman living in a thrush's egg blue villa with white stuccoed windows on the station road put it. Shadows blocked out the light at the half door, I.R.A. men on the run, tinker relatives coming to call. Martin was of a tinker family, the tribe of the Finnertys which had encompassed the whole of Ireland, he was assured. His own family had until recently traipsed the roads of Ireland and the historical data of these journeys reached the child; over fires on the fair Green in October, light cracking in the evening sky, to the sound of tin whistle music young Martin Finnerty gleaned the platter of tales. He grew up to the sound of old men's voices crunching over history, over great escapades, over profound and reverberating adventures. He ran in ruins, he leaped into beds of nettles in convents laid waste by Cromwell. He surveyed a town. His ancestors had come to the town once and left. Now they lived here, saddled as paupers but mindful, in him at least, of the shining waters of history, of the mastery of the roads. The only person who would listen to him was Witch McDonagh, a tall, angular-stanced girl whose black hair was banded by red ribbons and whose hands behind her back, foot in front, usually denoted unease. Lily McDonagh was branded by local children as a witch because of her black eyes.

When the other children were playing hopscotch Martin and Lily were engaged in games of history, he Shane O'Neill bowing to her Elizabeth on the white chalk demarcated roadway of Flea Lane. The sun hit the white chalk as the last games were enacted long after the other children had gone indoors. Charles I was bidding farewell to Henrietta Maria.

Lily was of a tinker family herself and the two awkward children compared notes; his had been the more triumphant one, they'd gotten the furthest in journeys, hers were confined to County Galway now, wild people, rough people, drinking people. She bowed to his more aristocratic reserve.

Whereas Martin's mother searched the meadows for wild honey, excavated flowers for secret herbs, Lily's parents were dull and shorn of energy. They grimaced at their measly cuisine. They existed in a darkness unalleviated by the strong broths and boiled pigs' feet of Martin's home. Martin ventured to this lonely den to lighten their burden and introduce colour, smiles, ruddy cheeks. 'O Martin Finnerty what's on your mind you little divil?' A lot, would have been the answer to that question.

When Martin and Lily were a little older the nature of the games changed; Lily, lankier than ever, stood in the shallows of the river, the pinkeens darting about her feet, her blue dress pulled up a little and Martin, in a ragged suit, white shirt now, gulping in her direction. She was Ruth to his Boaz. He was leading her away in the direction of clarinets.

Lily mourned the passing of childhood; she washed her hands in a chipped bowl, lingering on them. They curved now. They were instruments of romance, of divination. 'Lilian,' recently her mother had picked up this affectation in the house where she was char in which a member of a doctor's family was addressed as Lilian, 'Lilian,' her mother shrieked, 'Clean the floor.' So Lilian – or Lily – bent and graced the floor. She considered her boyfriend, plump now, a Neptune. 'Martin Finnerty I love you.'

The town had not changed much, a few war of independence and civil war ruins buttressed, when Martin went to work at the undertakers. Between funerals, despite the fact he'd only been educated as far as National school, he produced ledgers of history from underneath the counter and read them. These were obtained from the librarian. The librarian at the time was Protestant, she raised her spectacles underneath a slap of white hair and called in the voice of a major's wife in India: 'This will tell you a thing or two. This will tell you a thing or two.' Martin Finnerty followed up his childhood interest by becoming proficient in history. He delved deeply. He surveyed widely. He encompassed whole tracts of history. He became learned. The references piled up; he sat in his home in Flea Lane and, like a university professor, lectured his mother in the evening on the landing of the French in Killala in 1798. It was Irish history he studied needless to say and he discoursed on it; Lily McDonagh felt the slabs of history piled on top of her. She was like a corpse underneath the Protestant church.

'Champagne Charlie', 'Daisy, Daisy', the band always played the same tunes at the local hops, but they were interrupted now by a new diversion. Fool Finnerty, as he was now known, sat in a chair in the middle of the floor to tell tales of history; the middle-class youngsters of town stood back. Margaret McMahon, a surgeon's daughter from Balbriggan, stood forward. She was the loveliest girl in town, a Catholic, working as a bank clerk. The rugby lads, the cycle racing lads loved her. She stood so far forward, her shoulders erect, hair, amber and gold, falling on her shoulders, she nearly approached Martin. His favourite yarn was about Edmund Spenser, how he came to Cork, married Elizabeth Boyle, regularly addressed the moon, and then was driven on his bandy legs to Cork city. But he'd spent sufficient time in County Cork to smell the fields, the gold of the hay, and it was these smells that filled the dingy parochial hall; the harvest in the unending countryside, the wafting, the fidgeting strands of straw, became the harvest of County Cork in the late sixteenth century. Martin Finnerty restored magic to the lives of young people caught up in the mercenary prerogatives of a new country.

Margaret McMahon became the most talked about girl in town. She rode about on her bicycle as if nothing would stop her if she wished to cycle to the Riviera. The heads of old women riveted on her. Work was arbitrary for her. 'She must have a right collection of perfumes,' an old woman snarled. 'And she told someone she sleeps with a teddy-bear.' Her father whisked her off on holidays to Newcastle, County Down, and the way some people spoke of it it might have been Antibes or Saint Juan les Pins. On 23 August 1933 she became twenty-two and young rugby playing men in white shirts the crests of their clubs on discarded jackets, broke champagne by the river. There was a moon that night. Martin was not invited but he didn't care. Margaret was not so much a figure of love for him but one of a queen, of an empress, a kind of empress of feeling, good taste, aplomb. There was a figure comparable to her in Irish history. Eibhlin Dhubh ni Chonaill. Married to Art O'Laoghaire and when he was murdered by an English colonel she vied with his sister for the creation of a poem of lament.

Musk scents, embroidered gowns, duck feathered pillows had surrounded her, but in her mansion in Cork in which she moved among these things all of them were arbitrary. Margaret McMahon looked like a lady who'd play camogie for spite on the day her lover died and for whom her silken dresses were arbitrary; she stood on the main street and she read the advertisements in a metro in Paris.

Lily abided with Martin's admiration for Margaret; the girl from Flea Lane scrubbed dishes after her brothers' lunch. They worked in bogs, on building sites, they cleared rubbish, they dug drains. She pondered over the cracks, manifold as they were, on the blue rimmed white plates. The ground was slipping from under her; it wasn't just Martin's celebration of Margaret McMahon, it was her own position in life, a shadow in a kitchen. The green world of the town was shut off from her, the river banks, the fields beyond. Lily was crying and no one heard. Martin still postured at funerals; it was a wonder anyone harboured him at a funeral, a giant red clown-like carnation in his lapel. But he relieved people's burdens and usually had eloquent language by way of condolences. But it wasn't until Margaret McMahon drowned that something gave in Lily.

It was a June night, Margaret was sailing down the river by moonlight, she was with a young man, the boat hit a rock. The rest was town property. Her body was quickly whisked away, but the tragedy was turned over in every quarter in town. A memorial meeting was held in the parochial hall – the band incongruously played 'Greensleeves', an accordion player had come in from the country to bang off a mournful tune, rugby players looked impotent beside this musician who smelt of peat – and Martin Finnerty sounded off a lament which was the highlight of the evening. He'd composed the lament along the lines of one written by the Gaelic poet Raftery in memorial to humans and sheep drowned in a boating accident on the Corrib in 1820 and he enthroned himself on his chair in the middle of the floor to deliver it.

Hankies were produced in abundance. A line lingered in the mind. 'She had eyes like Tierra del Fuego butterflies.' What or where Tierra del Fuego was no one knew, but there was an agreement with silent stares that it suited Margaret McMahon. Martin wandered by the river at night and sought to commiserate with the moon. The moon acknowledged nothing. It teased him. From silver and pied it turned to gold. Lily McDonagh left town. She could have accepted Martin's admiration for Margaret but his elevated mourning, his penchant for the other world, finished her. With other girls she got a red bus from Galway to Enniskillen, and there, like a flock of migratory geese, cases in hands, they changed buses. Lily travelled to Belfast to work as a waitress. Her hotel was a meringue façaded one by the crusty Lagan waves. Lily dressed in black and white, a tiara of white on her head, and held out pineapple slices grinning with cream or slithering with French dressing to overfed Unionists. The letters arrived in bucketfuls: 'Dearest, dearest Lilian, my love for you threatens to overpower me and sweep me away. Lily, mo chroi, come home and we'll drive the fleas from Flea Lane.' Lily continued bringing pineapple and cream to fat Unionists, trespassing on gleaming floors.

Perhaps it was because of the lush waves of music on the edges of restaurant floors, but Lily was seized by a new interest – ballroom dancing. In a community hall off the Falls Road tutored by a smelly slimy priest, in the presence of fish-like girls in Irish dancing costumes, Lily took her first steps in ballroom dancing. Gradually she climbed a ladder. A hotel manager swept her to her feet and she was decked out in white taffeta in a hotel overlooking the lights of Belfast. Life was a spiral now. Smiling against a tobacco smelling hotel manager Lily announced to herself she'd escaped. Martin Finnerty could be traipsing the river bank at home for all she cared.

Eventually Martin too left the main street of the town where holes in the trousers had reached balloon proportions and an epidemic of eyes stared. He made his way to Belfast, first taking a train to Dublin, staying there in a semi-gutted bed-and-breakfast place on Amiens Street for a few days, wandering O'Connell Street, basking in the lights, licking ice-creams in a café, making idle chatter to the Grettas and the Eileens in the cafés, girls up from Limerick and Offaly, then leaving the smiling eyes, hugging his case to him, and journeying by train alongside the Irish Sea. The only myth that greeted him in Belfast was the war innuendo of 1690. Martin Finnerty in a long coat on a fine summer's day made his way through the ruined terracotta Victorian factories, across blood-stained cobbles, or cobbles on which you would imagine blood, to Lily's hotel.

Lily McDonagh in her hotel uniform, bowls of salmon mousse on a tray in her hands, the dust from scrabbling with floorboards under beds still on her hands, made known, 'Martin, I'm sick of history. I'm sick of all this creepy crawly nonsense. I have other pastimes in life now.' And with that she perked her nose in a position that made you gasp and hovered away on high heels with her tray. Martin, cap in hand, his brown tie with glittering emerald snakes on him, scented French strawberry perfume in her wake. 'Now where is she getting that?' he wondered, 'Not from Monsieur Poincaré.'

For two years Martin lived in Belfast unsuccessfully pursuing Lily. In a brown coat he travailed in a florist's cum hardware shop on Stranmillis Road. It was a hardware shop that specialised in tulip bulbs, carefully decked in boxes of clay outside. His digs, very humble ones, were on Leeson Street. His boots crunched home across

60

stones each night. In his sojourn in Belfast he was thrown into the Lagan once by young marauding Orange men, 'Baptised', on a black winter's night, he was brought into the hills once in a broken down Ford taxi and among the harvest gold told he was going to be made a martyr of, 'Saint Martin of Galway', a revolver pressed to his temple.

Other times he soothed both Catholics and Protestants at festive gatherings with interpretations of their mutual history; Martin made all history cohere with laughter, with wonder, with the eccentric and un-prejudged gesture.

A city stopped for him. Women folded their arms for him. But all the time he crawled to Lily she rejected him; she flashed her hand like a queen to dismiss him, turned on her heels, and disappeared into ballroom music.

Why he had come so far for one person was clear to him; Lily was the subterranean part of him, she was an asset of his life's history, a part of his childhood. For each person there is a companion whether we reach them or not. Lily McDonagh of the tribe of the McDonaghs was his.

It was a student priest who negotiated a settlement between them. Matt O'Hara hailed from Cushendun; he studied for the ministry at Maynooth, he wore spectacles, had pimples, was short and in the summer gave his service to the St. Vincent de Paul on the Falls Road. Martin, wasting handsomely away, fell into the realm of charity and Matt O'Hara tripped along a number of times to Lily McDonagh who had bobbed her hair now. Yes, she would join up with Martin on two conditions; provided he never spoke of history again and took up her consuming passion – ballroom dancing!

For Martin dancing was at first alien; in a blue white-spotted tie, the shopkeeper's assistant held back as a priest croaked the directions, the girls in Irish dancing costumes silenced, the women with haggard faces, but gradually Martin took the floor in a dream and waltzed with Lily to grace. Their special combination was so effective that soon they were representing the Falls Road ballroom dancing club at competitions all over Northern Ireland – and winning. Ballymena, Portadown, Antrim Town. Children cloaked in home-spun union jacks watched. Women, in whose eyes the Battle of the Boyne still raged, stared icily from their chairs. A man's hand disappeared into a mushy cake once, so spellbound was he by the flair of Lily and Martin. They danced on the moon over the mountains of Mourne. A band of ragged urchins in Celtic green beat triangles to celebrate when they won the Ulster championships, the children wending their way hesitantly along the Falls Road. At a harvest feast in 1936 by an oak table, an old man with a pint of Guinness called Lily over in her taffeta dress – she'd been dancing with Martin among the harvest fields – and whispered in her ear, 'I'd like to put my willy up your Fenian cunt.'

Perhaps it was that insult – Lily repeated it to Martin – or perhaps it was the flush of success which drove them from Ulster. Lily and Martin took the boat from Larne to Stranraer. Ireland had become too small a ballroom for them. 'Goodbye now the land of Cain. We're off to take the floor with Abel.' Martin still made his daft comments. The midsummer was drawn over the Irish Sea.

Martin's hand clutched Lily's. The world of British ballroom competitions opened to them. It wasn't all uphill. Martin and Lily got a bedsitter in Birmingham.

Instead of books of history, Martin in his waistcoat pored over comics now. A butcher lived nearby who called them Diarmaid and Gráinne, an Irish butcher. Always the impediment of history came to them. The invitations to competitions finally arrived. They were chosen. Lily bore the decrees from a box number in the post office because rumour had it their landlady opened other people's letters and burnt them, Lily on the Birmingham streets clutching the bits of paper in her hand. From John O'Groats to Land's End they danced, if you were later to believe Martin – actually from Aberdeen to Plymouth. She in white taffeta, Martin in silvery blue suits they took Britain by storm, doing an uncomplicated tango across the web of metropolises.

In Manchester a lady told her life story during a ballroom competition. 'I was raped five times as a child. Never recovered. Hate men.' Her voice drowned in a calypso. Martin took the floor with Lily and suddenly saw Henrietta Maria again. Try as hard as he could forgetting was impossible; he trudged the streets of a northern English city at dawn and remembered Ireland, light breaking over the river shallows, rabbits skirting them in the dawn, a man by the river walking with his dog. Martin wanted to be back home. He wanted to be unfolding stories again. Stories were part of him, eyes in the workhouse building, a spreading furnace of lies and truths and imaginary things. He was a spokesman for something he felt but what that something was he could not explain, only realize it was both a kind of game and a kind of recourse. Martin and Lily began losing competitions. The trail downhill was swift. In their room in Birmingham, Lily, standing, suddenly saw funerals crawling through Belfast, women strolling slowly behind them and red plastic flowers on the coffins because no one could afford to buy real flowers. Martin had accumulated a collection of pornography all around Britain, rags bought in transactions with shady characters in back streets, and inspired by these magazines, Martin had Lily undergo strange positions in their love making on a big lapsing bed in Birmingham. Perhaps it was her association of this with sin which made Lily see the outbreak of the Second World War as partly related to their guilt. In Plymouth in autumn 1939 a brass band sounded a dirge. Lily and Martin were among the onlookers. They'd taken a trip to a place where they'd scored a triumph once. On the boat back to Ireland in daylight, grabbing the rail of the deck laden with people like cattle, eyes anxious with sudden and uninvited unsettlement, a phrase beat again and again in Lily's mind 'To Hell or to Connaught.' A couple faded away into the fairyland of ballroom lights, blue and red, and Lily's hands curled about the railings. She had been found guilty.

She and Martin were married a year later – the wedding feast being held in the open air on Flea Lane. Pale blue high heels alighted on a patch of green. It was a sunny October day. Martin quoted elaborately from history in his address, the local mummers entertained with tin whistle music, a foxglove mauve hat was pulled on the bride's head. No one noticed her disgruntlement. There was no end to history then, talk of the Battle of Aughrim, of 1798, of the Great Famine, anecdote and incident. A year again after their wedding Martin was crowned king of the local fair, walking through town dressed like a leprechaun and bearing a gold tinsel sceptre. Lily had had it. Because of his former connections with the funeral trade, Martin was given the post of caretaker of the local cemetery when the vacancy occurred; it was endowed also with the gatehouse alongside it. Lily, pregnant, moved in with him. The children kept coming, quick on the mark, boys, girls, chipmunks she sometimes thought. Lizard-faced boys who grinned up at her. Children dispersed on reaching adolescence. Lily accepted a role once provided for her, wandering in the fields collecting comfrey and dandelion leaves, comfrey for bones, dandelion leaves for indigestion. Heather for love. The herbs, weeds, plants and ointments were unleashed from her fists. 'Witch McDonagh.' In the window on a black night Lily saw a woman driven crazy and witch-like. She expended little energy on her children then, she walked in the fields, her face became spectral white and her eyes wild and black. The mental hospital lay nearby, all eyes, all eyes in the night. Cherine, her youngest, much like herself, shook a glass ball with snow in it and Our Lady of Knock made an intrusive apparition to drunks, Saint John and Saint Joseph alongside her. One night Lily, rosary in her hands, walked into the river remembering a Franz Lehár waltz and a night in Birmingham when the stars merged

63

into the soul like snow and the ballroom floor glittered with a thousand drowned moons...

It was the blackness of the night her mother walked into the river and the blackness of the river which engulfed her which brought sweat to Cherine's face on a black night in November 1965 as she crossed the sea to England, standing on a deck, vipers of rain beating against her and eventually the rain indistinguishable from the tears which were streaming down her face under her old, much travelled scarf.

[4]

Cherine was sent to England to look after the children of her oldest sister who was pregnant for the fourth time. It was a tradition in her family for younger members to assist older members. Cherine's deaf and dumb sister had looked after Cherine and her father since the girl was eleven. Cherine left her father and her deaf and dumb sister bundled into the darkness of the house by the cemetery, bundled into the gestures, the stories. The request for help had come suddenly so Cherine was dashed off in a black taxi to the station, a scarf pulled down on her furrowed brow. Already she felt like a much older woman. She had not left in such a hurry as not to have encountered Eugene McDermott, however briefly, in the library. God, how tall he had grown, elegant even, red hair thrown back like a king. He looked at her straight. She felt childhood but she also felt other things. I have to leave. An old lady in black wormed her way up the lane opposite.

In London, in Charing Cross Road, she saw on a book cover a reproduction of a Renaissance painting of a young man which immediately brought back that moment and nearly suffocated her with its tenderness. Near that book another with Napoleon's portrait on the cover, his chipped chin, his dented eyes, the slime of black hair on his forehead springing her mind to Jeremy Hitchens, a more remote and shadowy figure than Eugene, but still one who headed the list of small town young men, who waited, candidates for her life, her affections, and her concern.

Trekking across Hackney Marshes, her red ribbon thrown back against the heaving clouds, the marshes became bogs, the high-rise flats mountains. Two little children with whom she had the relationship of a steed trailed alongside. They rode her back and beat her at intervals. Cherine glided in black. Black was the colour of London. Her sister lived in Hackney. Cherine had a small room, bare, the colour of gospels about it, she told herself. Here you heard the word of God. More accurately she was inveigled by the shrieks of a one-year-old baby. Cherine's sister sat up in bed, gloating over her luxurious pregnancy. Her pregnant stomach camped under bed clothes. Cherine's sister had auburn hair, wiped across her eyes. Once she'd lifted her skirts for middle-class boys on the headstones. A young man painted the title of a Drifter song in red lipstick across her navel. 'What cha gonna do?'

Now she scrutinized Cherine's movements lest Cherine was not fast enough, proficient enough at her duties. Cherine brought biscuits on a platter. Cherine already noticed age in the hands of her sister, curling inwards to seek solace of one another after the consumption of a cigarette. A girl, pony-tailed in her mind, passed the little hall where the brass band played on Sunday mornings and looked towards trees, autumnal like her hair, fallen chestnuts gaping open like her eyes, only to see herself older, sitting up in bed, making demands on a younger sister, unhappy. Part of the reason for this unhappiness took the form of an English gypsy, her husband, a Lancashire man, a mechanic, his apron sprawled with grime, and his eyes, over a very tasteful red check shirt (to Cherine's taste), pursuing Cherine as if she was a vision of future seductiveness. When it all became too much, her sister's siren blasts, the extravagence and illumination of her brother-in law's eyes, the whinging, the clasping of sinking children, Cherine took a coat, descended a lift, flitted out by the exit where the walls read – 'Mrs Dewick boils snakes' – and escaped. Hands in her pockets, she took Charing Cross Road by storm. The multitudes gave way, the girls in ashen mini skirts with lunar mascara, the languishing boys with frontal drooping crests of hair, the men with bowler hats beside bus-stops. The faces of pop singers, jazz singers cowered in the womb-like duskiness of record sleeves. It was 1965 and Cherine Finnerty had come to town.

'I grew up in a small town in County Mayo. My father the local doctor. They did not like me, my family. I tilled the fields, I pulled up turnips. I was a country boy. They were townspeople. There was a workhouse in our town, a park a statue of a British colonel. At seventeen I took the bus to Dublin and crossed to England. Been here ever since. The letters stopped coming. My brothers and sisters are doctors now. Me, I've been on the wine this many a year. No use is there, no hope when nobody loves you.' It was the Continental Café,

Charing Cross Road. An Irish tramp spoke. Dusty Springfield routinely plainted 'I don't know what to do with myself.'

'Darling. Honey, Sweetheart. Will you hold the baby while I pull up my stockings.' An Irish lady tramp ran up to Cherine on the Embankment, overlooking the Thames, entrusting her with a weighty baby, a two litre bottle of Powers.

By Charing Cross Station the pavements were swept with the down and outs of Ireland, these sleeping. 'I grew up in a small town in County Mayo. My father the local doctor.' Cherine surveyed those the towns with the workhouses and the golf courses did not want. The small town dustbins of Ireland had opened and let them out. She too was among the escapees.

Of course it was not as simple as all that; she could not disappear from home at will. Her sister's permission had to be gained. Cinderella flitted back up Charing Cross Road and disappeared into the welter of neon and pop-songs.

'Mulvanney. Alan. *A Cavalier Against Time.*' In the library, her children destroying valuable books, a bunch of golden chrysanthemums at their height of humid openness beside her, Cherine looked up an old byword. No luck, no sign of him or his book; it was her private joke, her private mark of respect to me, to Eugene, to the small town she came from and the whimsical chats with two unusual lads.

Damian was a different class of lad; black; fine hair snuggling in curls into his head, a black jacket open on him revealing a doll-like and amiable chest. She bumped into him in the library, a day she was transporting a mountain of books about toys of the various ages. In the park behind a terracotta lavatory as the winter sun snaked down he lifted her mini skirt – bought on Portobello Road – and savoured her thigh with his fingers. 'A swan's wing,' she christened the spot that night in bed. The legends of Ireland assembled in her mind, a hailstorm of swans, a young man and woman on the same white horse, the destitute images of the deprived. She no longer suffered deprivation; her flesh had been grazed. She could live without legends now.

'Damian wait there. Damian mind Mark.' Damian held Mark as Cherine examined floral dresses in Portobello Road. But it was the moments in Portobello Road alone, without her makeshift boyfriend, her exiled spirit was most vented; there was a kind of symmetry to solitude, an acknowledgement of it by a man with a talking parrot, by a blind Irish accordionist who sang songs like 'Danny Boy', like 'The Mountains of Mourne' to a swaying motion, by an Irish tramp outside a pub holding a glass of cider to her. Cherine picked her way through the procession on Portobello Road. On an icy December morning she mentally composed a letter to Eugene McDermott.

'Eugene, it's cold here, the cabbages have frost in them but inside every cabbage, every item of clothing, every face is a kind of wonder world, a children's palace, a room warm with people and fires. I am like the little match-girl. You, Eugene, are the tin soldier. I hope we meet in another story book which allows the little match-girl and the tin soldier to be in the same story.' A fire spurted in Portobello Road, the image lit up by a little match-girl's matches, a fire in a big house on the main street at home, a boy beside it, his jersey brown and running with patterns, his eyes alive with eagerness for life. If the legends of Ireland were gone something remained demanding to be articulated, library books borrowed as a child, shared images, whispered conversations. Eugene McDermott encountered her coming the other way on Portobello Road but a vision of him in the street, a sense of intractable longing, of shared wonderment at passing clothes, eyes and regressive, curled up cabbages.

'On Boxing Day we took to the sea in our best clothes by the Petit Piton mountain near Soufrière. An old man with white hair played a guitar and we stayed out on the bay until it was dark and the bay lit up with lanterns and we sang songs in Spanish or French or Creole.' On Boxing Day Cherine listened to Damian's mother mesmerise them about home as she knitted mindlessly. Black men behind her poised darts at a dartboard. Christmas crackers lay about, vacated of their wares. Damian's face was in his hand, a pop magazine lying unrecognized by him. At home skeletal mummers would be lining the pavement outside the burnt-out workhouse. 'And once or twice we dived into the clear waters in our suits and dresses, dickie bows, silk dresses and swam and swam until we grew exhausted and then returned to the shore in boats and danced beside bonfires until our bodies became dry again.'

Cherine in black backed up Charing Cross Road. Her skirt had grown shorter. Her lips were red, the mascara of her eyes suddenly ignited with neon. She wished her varnished finger-tips could hold a cigarette but she was incapable of smoking. A frizz of black curls stood in place of her hair. Her audience, gaping, was a swarm of colours. Alan Mulvanney. Montgomery Clift. Sabina Finnerty. The glamorous, the magical, the elevated were summoned to her side, her sole knowledge of transcendence. Damian was a thing of the past. She had enraptured London. But still there was a request in her, a letter sealed and about to be delivered. There was something a main street in a small town still demanded of her before exile became permanent and glamour overwhelming; she had to touch someone's white shirt, toss his orange hair, make love to – to childhood, the domain of childhood that was still in her. 'Eugene McDermott.' His name echoed in the backroom of a flat in a high-rise block in Hackney. The door opened. Cherine's brother-in-law entered, much as expected for weeks, carefully closed the door, turned with alertness to the knob, confronted her, his eyes naked, approached, took her in his arms, fondled her cold cream breast with his brown nicotine and work stained hand, his hand searching under her black blouse until it was firmly placed on the breast and was ascertaining its size and its recent growth. Cherine said nothing. The man left. A different girl stood, a kind of mannequin.

In a few days, she was on a boat back to Ireland. Her sister suspected without knowing. The baby hadn't arrived but Cherine was relieved of her duties. On the deck Cherine confronted the sea but couldn't find the position of her existence as she'd made the journey in the opposite direction. London had briefly but determinedly exported Cherine to Ireland.

[5]

Eugene McDermott's parents were married on 2 September 1939. The marriage feast was held in the open air by the Shannon. It was a golden day. Some women were marooned in the fields, awaiting the food. The guests gathered about an oak table, mainly her people as his were for the most part dead. An old man smiled as his mind settled on a Victorian wedding in this very spot, a bride in dripping white standing behind the haycocks as an accordionist started up 'The Lark in the Clear Air'.

His people – the groom's – had originally come from the far west, South Connaught, harsh land, inhospitable land; the terrain served up to the native Irish as replenishment as they'd forged west in the exodus. Mr. McDermott's people had tired of enslavement and moved east. In their part of Ireland moving east meant one of two things, entering a mental hospital or attaining prosperity. In the McDermott's case prosperity was attained, their name above stores and pubs on main streets in east Galway towns. Their homes were big and made of limestone. Big women ruled the houses. Sometimes a lady journeyed from the west in a mule and cart, a clay pipe in her mouth, but she was unwelcome. In Mr. McDermott's case the hurley was forsaken for the more precise and British rugby ball. Already, as a young man, he commanded a hardware store. He stood outside it, looked west, saw nothing but the shining brass knockers of the country houses he visited on his bicycle, the blue dresses of Protestant girls, and the cycles he raced, and the rugby balls he kicked. His parents were dead. His brothers had mainly fallen out with one another because of conflicting business interests. A sister, a nun, was locked in a convent in Tasmania. Red-haired, red carnation in his button-hole, a rainbow of freckles on his nose, his chestnut eyes dappled with darker brown, he looked towards the Shannon, preliminary Guinness on his mouth, and remembered nothing.

She'd had seven sisters and one brother. Her people were Midland people and so their accents jarred, flat, unswerving accents like the landscape. It was of her sisters and her brother she thought as the food was served, farm produce. Her silver spoon diving into the juice of the mutton. Each of her sisters had worn a long veil mildewed and made yellow ochre with age, embroidered by an Irish nun in the south of Spain for their holy communions. That veil was like the kiss of death sitting on their heads. One by one the girls died, at first slowly, a small number in childhood soon after their holy communions. Esther. Maria. Bertha. Their photographs first taken in that veil in a photographer's studio in Mullingar, the brown photographs in a farm drawing room now. Bertha. Martha, Esther In 1911 the survivors were herded into a car and driven to the Eucharistic Congress in Dublin, Mrs. McDermott's brother, his ears standing out like an impish boy's in a comic cartoon. There were the dances then, odysseys through lanes bordered by poppies in the dusk in Ford Vauxhall Tudors. The cars verged onwards, heaving their cargo of weightless girls. But some of the dancers died too. The nun who'd donated the holy communion veil wrote from Spain that the will of Christ was strange and now Christ would take them into his home and marry them.

When so many of her sisters had been eroded as to make the girls on bicycles seem scarce, Mrs. McDermott stepped into a laneway and looked at a young man who lived up the road. He lived with his mother, a dark woman. Mrs McDermott's father forever warned her against this family. They did not go to Mass. The young man studied in Dublin. His studies were nearly over. The father had exited to the hereafter and, judging by local opprobrium for this family, in his case

69

the hereafter was probably purgatory. Hell was reserved for an identical misdemeanour in women. To get to this young man's house you passed the houses of two Protestant ladies, of a parson who addressed his cat 'My love for you Jonathan surpasses the love of women', of an English woman who had Jews from Ravenna staying from time to time. The road was narrow, ribbony and, unusual for this area, hilly. Mrs. McDermott had read books in childhood, big books; had ceased reading books. Looking at this young man revived that emotion. He was an exotic and elaborate vernacular on a page. Afterwards she would forget about it, she would not try to remember it and if she did remember it she would punish herself for it, but she was in love. Being in love in Ireland in 1935 was like writing a list for the grocers; harvest fields, oak trees, bicycles, country butter, salving dandelion leaves for nettle burns, ruined castles, sore ankles, laughter. Her head in a field dipped and looked at a scorched ankle. She said nothing. They said little to one another. There was no time to say anything. Her father discovered and then she seized her closest friend, the bicycle, and rode all those miles to Dublin to see him, meeting him in an ice-cream parlour under a blown-up photograph of Venice. Still few words were exchanged. She had no education. He had much. She had black hair, chipped teeth. Her smile was a bouquet of red hawthorn he said. The priest at Mass in a church in a harvest field prayed for Franco. The host was raised in battlefields in Spain, the spent Irish country boys lying in uniform. 'Virgen de Irlanda ruega por nosotros.' In an ice-cream parlour in Dublin a black-haired, curly headed young man articulated his feeling about Spain under a blown-up picture of the Piazza San Marco in Venice – one pigeon idling near the camera! – and for the first time Mrs. McDermott was totally aware of other anthems, other prayers, other supplications. She remembered catching sight of male genitals underneath football shorts on a village green, pulling her own dress down in embarrassment, turned away and then on a moonlit night on a hill near her home turned back, embracing forcefully the young man who'd said that Franco was a fascist in a Dublin ice-cream parlour and that the Irish bishops were 'stooges'.

When he went to fight for Spain, taking a suitcase across the harvest fields, his long coat on him, she received his letters. They entered tremulously into her hands in the house of his mother.

Almeria, December 1937
Though it is winter the colours of the flowers are wild and wonderful.

Valencia, 14 December 1937

I danced to a tango last night. On a beach an old man plays 'Silent Night' on a melodion. The weather's cold and a foghorn blows.

Madrid, New Year's Eve 1937

The enemy is near. Time and the enemy of love.

In a uniform, red handkerchief about his neck, a young Irishman fought and was not heard of. No postage stamps, exotic like the flowers of Almeria, in his mother's home, no trips to that house, the smell of butter and truant mice there, the redolence of military portraits. His mother was dying. She died in April. Mrs. Mc-Dermott's father sat over the body as though over the hearth. He lit a pipe. Tall candles burned. No more was heard of the young man. He disappeared into legends of banshees in the fields of childhood, into ghost stories told over a furnace of an autumn fire. The young man who left for Spain did not return. Nettles wavered outside his house, a burnt out crater in her. A shadow skimmed the nettles. She put her hands to her face as though blocking out the shadow. But she was burning a part of herself. She leaped on her bicycle, travelled to a church, prayed for her sisters and omitted a prayer for a young man lost in Spain. But there was still grief, more silence than grief; she collected cigarette paper for the missions. She played with its tobacco smelling tinsel by a fire. A young man was calling for her. He was from the west. He wound his way up the lane to the house, his hat in his hand. He had a red nose. Her father, sitting by the fire, noticing her languishing at and wary of the prospect of his daughter losing this young man with mercantile tips to his fingers, roused his red eyed and distant daughter and in a kitchen smelling of two newly baked loaves of brown bread, standing, declared a mountain of pound notes awaited her across the Shannon.

'A mountain of pound notes.' First time she visited his town, for a dress dance, merchants' wives eyeing her, she saw the pound notes swimming about her, laughing in her face, grinning little elfin pound notes, leprechaun pound notes. One of them took her hand and led her in a waltz.

The local brazen woman, a girl with falling black curls, valiant, slightly scarred bare arms, in a blue dress, hands on the table, entertained some young and eager farmers now, their forelocks naturally blond or blond from the sun. Moira this girl was called and

71

her name reverberated through hawthorn bushes in spring like the word sin; though sin was practised in autumn as well as in spring. Tonight ... eyes were averted. 'Our beloved holy Father'. Mrs. McDermott's father, a slight, bald man, his Adam's apple like a mushroom, rose to make a speech and at once invoked the presence of the snake-like pope. The man's eyes narrowed as he proclaimed the many, credited virtues of his new son-in-law; holy purity, even, thrown into the bag. The purity of rugby players, shopkeepers, young men who kept God's commandments in regard to sex and abstained from carnality until madonna-like wives were conjured in their lives. As the man spoke the bride noticed someone not listening, walking away from the gathering. Her sister. Her oldest and only surviving sister, a sister who'd always been somewhat remote and abstained from the many indulgences of family life. Maybe it had been because of her superior age. She'd read widely. She'd travelled to Germany and to Bucharest. She'd been in England. A year before, after years of celibacy, reading, hard work in Dublin, she'd married a rich horse-breeder from Meath. He was a jovial sort, trout faced, puckish and red featured, took a floor in a Galway hotel overlooking Eyre Square for the week of the Galway races each year, entertaining his racing comrades with Guinness on these premises and singing the raucous songs 'Glorio, glorio to the bold Fenian men.' Her brown suit was neatly cut, a blue brooch with a white cameo of a mother and child on her breast. Her brown hair was in a heavy bun, her face gaunt, despite its breadth, and serious. What was she thinking of? Pigeons taking flight in an early morning square in the grey city of Bucharest with the mists of autumn prevailing? A hotel in Berlin run by an Irish woman from Skerries who wrapped herself in a brown cardigan on winter nights and enumerated the list of nuns from her village who had assailed the outside world with the gospel? A hospital in London where she'd worked, old people dying, women ebulliently and sullenly looking at death? Her eyes above her white silk blouse with its neat, slightly browned ribbon, flickered in remembrance of posters, newspaper photographs, marches. Suddenly as the vowels of her father fell behind swans rose from the Shannon, a troop of them, their necks craning hungrily upwards, golden beads dripping from them, a cataract of beads. A year later she was dead.

The Lord is my shepherd; I shall not want.
He maketh me to lie down in green pastures: he leadeth me beside the still waters.

He restoreth my soul: he leadeth me in the paths of righteousness for his name's sake.

Yea, though I walk through the valley of the shadow of death, I will fear no evil: for thou art with me; thy rod and thy staff they comfort me.

Thou preparest a table before me in the presence of mine enemies: thou anointest my head with oil; my cup runneth over.

Surely goodness and mercy shall follow me all the days of my life: and I will dwell in the house of the Lord for ever.

In a fur coat, purchased for her by her husband in Dublin, Mrs. McDermott shivered on the women's side of the church, her husband kneeling on the other, hat by his side, the last of the light beating on the reds and blues of the stained glass window; the priest's nose, scorched red and purple from the African sun, illuminated, his surplice hanging threateningly, Mrs. McDermott's fur coat blackened and wizened as her face reached for her hands, and her sorrow was squashed in the well of tears which had accumulated in the palms of her hands.

Her sister had died, like all the others, from tuberculosis but this one had meant more to her than the others, older, strange, cogent. Mrs. McDermott tried to hold in her grief but she kept seeing the woman walking by the Shannon, her face both serious and doubting, the future of those eyes now a coffin, the gathered mourners, the cessation of all walking.

In the car, back across the Shannon, Mrs. McDermott felt but was no longer able to articulate to herself how this old sister had held her life together; she'd been a force at her side, an awareness, an anchorage, a grave knowledge of the world that made all problems diminish and replaced fear with mystery.

Since coming to this town Mrs. McDermott had been introduced to all the spinsters and matrons, women in primrose dresses eyeing her over primrose tea cups flecked with robin red. She had been an object of study for these women. A newcomer to the town, a shopkeeper's wife, her hands folded in front of her pregnant stomach. In her third month of pregnancy her brother, his hair already sweeping with baldness across his dormouse face, ran away to England, joined the merchant navy. 'Sacred Heart of Jesus. Sweet Jesus.' Mrs. McDermott's mother prayed. Like some before, he'd crossed the harvest fields with a suitcase, heading towards a tiny rural station.

Her husband played rugby. He gallivanted on the mental hospital rugby pitch on winter afternoons that were already nearly black as the mud on the pitch, eagerly passing the ball to his rugby comrades also in their blue and white striped jerseys. Mrs. McDermott shuddered away from these blackened afternoons. She remained in the kitchen. Geese cried over the river outside. Inside herself, standing in the kitchen, the lights not on, she held her hands in front of her. To where had she come? A town with a big mental hospital, its outbuildings stretching into the bogs, west of the Shannon, a main street. In child-birth she saw herself, a girl in white, standing beside her oldest sister, a companion for her incandesced, her sister about to embark on a journey, purple lilac falling on rusted railings, her sister in a brown suit, her eyes already eyes in a Mass card. Mrs. McDermott's husband laughed, swigged back Scotch. The laughter gurgled. A war was being fought in the outside world, but here shadows picked their way along the main street.

Mr. McDermott looked upon his little daughter as an intriguing and alien doll. He continued downing Scotch, playing rugby, laughing. The laughter reached a crescendo. Mrs. McDermott's brother died in England, a girl with long, red hair by his side. She walked her daughter. She attended Mass. Halting, she passed remarks with other women. Our Lady of Lourdes, Our Lady of Fatima were popular subjects of conversation, and patterns for embroidering firescreens, the weather, yes, the awful, dirty Galway weather. Always clouds flaunting themselves, swelling black clouds coming in from the Atlantic. A woman sped her daughter in a go-car along the main street. They visited Bray, they visited Ballybunion, her husband, daughter and herself. But always among the ice-cream vendors overlooking the inlets of the west of Ireland there was something missing. Cliffs carved out in seaside towns, precipices, gulls bore in from America. 'May the mother of God give me a son.'

The mother of God looked at her in the local church and her eyes said Mrs. McDermott's request would be granted.

Those years, black, lonely years, the years of the forties, a main street, an endless stroll with her husband and daughter along a country lane when greyness was welling up in the afternoon. In the year of Our Lady 1950 she became pregnant again – from ice-cream cones in a west of Ireland seaside resort, from gulls and men peddling pictures of the Virgin Mary, the Virgin dolled up in appropriate summer clothes, orange, white, mystical and levitating crowns on her head – Mrs. McDermott's son was born in the spring of 1951.

'Oh Eugene get up out of that.' He was immediately a strange child, orange-haired, plonking himself in a pool of dirty water as though in the sea. A sister flashed a jealous stare at him. Black, wild haired,

Mrs. McDermott sauntered on a beach in County Kerry, her skirt rolled up, her feet bare, her life, her 'red hawthorn bouquet', chipped teeth smile complete. The gulls arrived graciously from America, settled on the sand. A tinker woman pulled a black shawl around her and observed a lovely young woman with her son.

'Eugene plays with dolls. It's not like behaviour you'd expect of little boys. He sits in the yard, pulls dresses over their heads, fixes their dresses, forces combs through their hair. Maybe he'll be a fashion designer some day. He's a strange child, not like a little boy. He loves dolls. God, I don't know what to say Mrs. Maloney. His father thinks him crazy. His father doesn't know what to make of him. Still Mrs. Hanratty says he's bright at school. And Sister Antonio is crazy about him. What are you wearing to the dress dance? The weather's going to change, isn't it? It looks like snow. When will we get a bit of decent weather? I'm frozen stiff. Well, goodbye, Mrs Maloney.'

Eugene pulled combs through dolls' resisting hair all right, he smoothed dresses on the nakedness of dolls, being especially tender with their barely assertive breasts. He had his own special supply of ribbons, bold reds and emeralds. He was an expert in hair arrangements. His sister left for a convent school in Galway. She was swamped in chocolate brown. Her whole stance was silenced. Her hair curled outwards. Only her eyes reminded you of childhood. In the meantime Eugene had graduated to producing plays. His theatre was in the shed. A fat lad was especially talented and, summer after summer, landed the roles of Our Lady of Lourdes or Our Lady of Fatima, accepted a white bath towel on his head and when his hands were joined in apparition the stage time and time again going from under him. Enemy gangs invaded and brought chaos. War was not uncommon in the backyard by the river. Mr. McDermott played his rugby, drank, having given the child some of his time, then having turned away. Eugene defied description. But sure he'd be bright at school, wouldn't he? He might even make a priest. Mrs. McDermott was daring in her expectations. There were times Eugene just read, closing himself off with a book. Eugene. Dazzling illustrations burned before him. He was in another world. And then sometimes he sneaked off, with the tinker's daughter, Cherine Finnerty.

Mrs. McDermott's daughter did her leaving certificate, went to Dublin, joined the civil service. A faded Mrs. McDermott appeared at dress dances. Mr. McDermott still played rugby. Rugby games raged when he played them. There'd been no son. As well as moving away from Eugene there was a gap now between Mr. McDermott and

Mrs. McDermott, a visible gap, sometimes as graven as the bridge dividing east from west of Ireland in Athlone. There were new litanies, new prayers, new priests. Eugene seemed unaware of his parents' concern for him. His theatre flourished. Dracula made an appearance, peeping through curtains, and a plethora of banshees and dullaháns. Mites screamed and were frightened for life.

When Eugene was thirteen, just before he began at secondary school, Mrs. McDermott one day suddenly had enough, stormed into his theatre when, alone, he was fixing the sack curtains, tore them down, tore the paraphernalia of scenery down, hit Eugene mercilessly and forcefully on the face. 'Time to grow up, Eugene, time to grow up.' Eugene just stared, the freckled spot red, his hand going to it absently. That night, as it was just after midsummer light still in the sky, in her bedroom, under a wedding photograph of herself and her husband, on the oceanic-blue, billowed quilt Mrs. McDermott sat smoking a cigarette, the tip lighting up like a signal, the lights not on, and gradually, even with the methodical smoking, tears came, at first quietly, then violently, a rage, an impotence of tears, finally a scream. She went to the window, light leaving the sky, spoke to the swifts and wondered where her marriage had gone, where her son had gone and very desperately tried to see a girl in a holy communion frock in Maytime, a Spanish nun's veil on her head, for that alone made sense, a ceremony, hands joined in prayer long ago in a field by the Shannon before the retinue of deaths began, before the procession of tears began, before . . . She saw Eugene's face again, reddened, staring at her and she just wanted to hit it again, hit it until he cried.

[6]

Christmas 1965, Eugene McDermott visited Dublin. He'd been looking forward to this visit so much. He got a bus from the station to his sister's place in the mountains. It was dark and about to snow.

His sister made tea. Though young she was old. A civil servant. This house she shared with another girl and the girl was away. Eugene was surrounded by dead things, inarticulate chairs. It was all modern, gleaming in the kitchen. His sister, standing, stared.

She had been used to treating Eugene as a problem; it was a standard procedure in her family. He too standing confronted her, in

76

a long coat now. There had been times she'd returned from boarding school in Galway city to be informed of Eugene's latest madness. Was this child the stuff mental hospitals were made of? Eugene. He was red-haired, rather handsome, but one treated him like one did a country in Africa, the poor, the homeless or, in the most transcendental of moments, the tinkers. The tinkers were just beginning to be the objects of charity in Ireland. Eugene deserved charity. So his sister, member of many Catholic societies, asked him how school was and gave him biscuits.

Herself, she'd been a star at school, especially in mathematics. She worked in the Department of Finance now. Patiently she waited for a man. No man would come. She prayed more earnestly than her mother. She had none of her mother's looks or her father's, her features were like porridge. Virginity was stored up in her as in a granary. There were few comments she could pass with her brother without feeling she was going over the top, so silence came and suddenly you looked out the window and saw snow.

On a street in Dublin Eugene walks along. It is Christmas 1965. He wears a long coat. He has come from the mountains. The neon splashes around him, it surrounds him and as he walks I see another face in another time, Alan Mulvanney. Why do I connect these two people? Innocence, vulnerability, Eugene has freckles, Alan had none, his skin was cream, his black hair oily even, like a Spaniard's, but their features merge at one point. As their twin figures walk through Dublin it's as if they're going to say something – their lips verge on a trembling – though they are alone. It is Christmas 1941, it is Christmas 1965 and then you see it, over the eyes an intensity, a furrowing, a perplexity that is similar. Alan has been writing his novel. It's been a hard night. His landlady has been particularly garrulous about her son in England. The lights of the North Wall sweep alongside the black and withdrawn tide. He took a bus in. His landlady has been loud about the prospects of her son being bombed and for some unknown reason appealed to Joan of Arc to save him. Joan of Arc. There's a room in that house where Alan composes, swans, cavaliers, but beyond the swans and cavaliers a different language, an alternative language. Why all this yearning to be different? The world's being murdered. The vaults of tenderness are being invaded. But you need to resist don't you? So Alan is making a novel as he walks along. An old man's face lights up, newspaper headlines. Alan sees old men among the ruins of foreign cities. One day no people will be left he tells himself. The world will be overrun by destruction. Unless ... Eugene's mind is a riot with lights now.

For months it's been lonely. He's looked forward to this trip but now that he's here and approaches the Liffey he forgets himself and his own problems and – magically – remembers a poem I told him about, written by a friend of my mother's, about a doomed snowman. In 1941 as Alan approaches the Liffey he too remembers that snowman. It is Christmas 1941, Christmas 1965, two young men walk away from the Liffey, leaving a space filled by doubt, by pain, but also by excitement.

[7]

In March a priest dying of cancer described the death of Keats in class. The priest was not really old, fiftyish, black hair stubbed by ash. He wore a black cassock. Lenten darkness had accumulated in the air as he confronted his class. Boys listened, attentive because this was a force of imminent death speaking. There was a moribund and silent interest. Eugene sat, hands joined on the desk in front of him. I reclined at the back of the class, in a white jersey. The priest commenced with his tale as if nothing could interfere with his telling it, neither death or the boys' lack of interest in literature.

The English teacher had grown up in County Clare; he'd been one of a large family, theirs had been a house on a cliff of green grass. The sea was nearby; a village. In autumn the many children waded among the harvest on this steep incline of grass beside the house. A grandmother, a woman sitting in, brooding in and smothered by the shadow of the kitchen, the area around the open hearth her domain, urged the English teacher to the priesthood. She gave the snowy, bony kneed boy the idea of it. A Brigid's cross was ravelled above the door. The boy stood in wonder in the threshold light, confronting his grandmother. She upheld relics for him, demonstrated the remains of the saints, a hair, a piece of sackcloth; waved flaming purple rare rock flowers from the Burren which sometimes visited in a trap, a tattered umbrella above her in the sun. Flowers too were manifestations of God.

A young man, he journeyed up to Dublin, being taken in a trap to the station in Ennis. From Dublin he jumped on a red bus to Maynooth. Maynooth was a black place. Tremulous lipped, tremulous eyed, he studied for the priesthood. In the college in Maynooth was a room boarded up. The forces of evil inhabited this room. Chairs had taken flight in it and young priests had thrown themselves from its window. In the mind were rooms boarded up and thrown into chaos. Clare was left behind and flowers. The shadow of the priesthood fell over him.

A priest he returned to Clare to entrench literature; he taught in a boys' school. He confronted boys smelling of mucus and inappropriate ointments. 'A thing of beauty is a joy for ever.' Poetry dissolved into an antechamber of the mind, eyes powdered; he left for Rome.

Often now he poured over books about Rome; Rome, the eternal city. A young Irish priest sauntered through the streets of Rome. But mind you he wasn't that young, between thirty and thirty-five. How he loved the Via Appia and the fountains. Life became wonderful there. He spied on eternity. It was after the war. People were churning with agitation; the very air was frolicsome. He stayed in the Irish College. There had been a broken sundial there which registered nothing. Eventually he became lonely for Ireland. But one day, before leaving, he encountered a young man from Athlone whom he remembered because on a day the sun was crumbling down – one of those Roman sunsets, all fire, all furnace, all magnificence – the young man, over a glass of red wine, began mumbling on about the Irish defeat at Aughrim, the details of it, dogs devouring the dead. The young man had worn an onyx ring on the second finger of his right hand. Then he'd wandered off, into the sunset, hands in his pockets, into the many sunsets, the battle marches, the laments. Suddenly, like lightning, you were aware of a heritage. You were aware of a nation. You were aware you were Irish. This young man had illuminated this for you.

Could he have been the same young man who'd been rumoured to have had a nervous breakdown on the premises of the Irish College itself? God knows. But anyway you remembered him, strolling into the aftermath of market marigolds, and the torpor of the evening, and the wet of the market places refreshed and trickling with rivulets of water.

The priest returned to Ireland; Dublin airport, the fumbling gestures of grabbing a case wrought a kind of slowing, a relaxation that the glasses of red wine were over, the retinue of them. You got a bus into the city centre. Dublin was a shroud. Evening came, hesitantly, neon. An Irish priest blackened by the Roman sun, in a black cassock, took – uncertainly, a fugitive look on his face, a gaze towards Heaven in his eyes – a red bus to the school in the country where he still remained.

The school, when he arrived, had only recently moved from a site taken over by the mental hospital. The new demesne was grandiose. It suited the privileged. Boys aimed javelins. The eyes of old priests feasted on boys. For years old priests had fought to make this school a kind of public school but they were rewarded with the ignorant sons of Irish farmers. With the years pretensions declined – the manners, the edification of the country boys became even less – unruly hordes from the town were admitted through the gates as day pupils. At the present stage I headed the list of the riotous. But English literature had not failed the priest. John Keats and Gerard Manley Hopkins, his favourite poets, held their own. He breathed life into their poetry. John Keats wrote 'Ode to the Nightingale' under a plum tree in Hampstead over and over again. Gerard Manley Hopkins, the cassocked Jesuit, surveyed before death the nasturtiums in the gardens of University College Dublin. '"Beauty is truth, truth beauty," – that is all Ye know on earth, and all ye need to know.' The tennis playing boys in white, the half naked young gardeners all became part of a circle of poetry; poetry was the Mass, the celebration of it, the upholding of the eucharist. Poetry was a slowness. Poetry was God. Poetry was a daily transcendence in a rotting and lightless classroom.

But even poetry is challenged sometimes; even the slowness it brings about, the hovering on the eternal. The previous year the priest had been told he had cancer and would die of it in some years; a slow cancer. In autumn he'd returned to Clare, trudged the harvest fields in his cassock. He picked his steps slowly, looking down. 'Season of mists and mellow fruitfulness. Close bosom-friend of the maturing sun; Conspiring with him to load and bless With fruit the vines that round the thatch-eves run.' The nearby town was neon lit in the evening. The sea was pale blue and effervescent in the day. The world had changed. Machines mowed the fields. He turned to the low-lying land and wondered had his life been in vain, tissue of thrown away poetry. In a farm kitchen he felt emptied. The clock ticked. The elders lay under the ground. Rome did not come to help; the geraniums in the windows, the lichen on the white-washed walls. There was no sun in his soul. His fingers grabbed a thimble.

The opening of the year at school felt kinder to him. Avenues of mist received him. The English teacher meandered on a path which meandered towards death, but perhaps he saw that death needn't necessarily be an annihilation, but a kind of response to a lifetime of trying. Boys, middle-aged, would remember shards of poetry. Occasional trees were piqued with red. Horses, stationary, refused to snortle in the fields. Walking slowly, head down, hands behind his back he had a picture. His death would fix an image for ever; boys lined up in white briefly elated with Keats. Those brief moments of elation, those times when his words cut through lives and minds would be intensified and expanded with his death; it would create an eternity, an ongoing intrigue with his life, his attempt to communicate – he paused in his thoughts – things of beauty.

Maybe, just maybe today as he told the story of Keats' death another face overshadowed memory, a most luminous face, the broken words, a young man from Athlone on the Via Appia in 1950 who haunted, who remained, who still excited by way of his words, his love of words, his enchantment with words and the childlike sparkle in his eyes.

'In the autumn of 1820 John Keats left England. He knew he was leaving it behind for the last time. On the deck of the boat his friend and companion Joseph Severn came from behind and touched his wrist. Low sooty winter clouds scudded over Dover.'

Eugene McDermott fidgeted with a pen; Eugene the dazed eyed. He looked up with those eyes as if to reproach the priest on some aspect of his tale, then returned to his fidgeting.

'On board was a young woman also dying of consumption. Keats needed open windows. She convulsed with open windows. Out at sea a Portuguese ship of war approached them threateningly and Keats – on a rare day of venturing out on deck – sighted three whales.'

The split between Eugene McDermott and myself was uppermost in my mind today; I hugged the corner of the chip shop still, reluctantly. Eugene stayed at home. We were of like mind but worlds apart. I wanted these worlds to cohere, and so manifest something – something as simple as affection

'Lying in bed on a boat John Keats felt a poem coming, but this poem had a different outline from any poem he had written. He couldn't see it as yet, he was blind to it and yet he knew it was there and deciphered its margins with phantom fingers.'

The nights were the worst for Eugene, being of family you didn't understand who didn't understand you. Sometimes under pressure of a nightmare he groped to a window, pajama top hanging off, as if to throw himself out but he was always stopped by something, the blackness outside, bitten by skeleton lights. He returned to his bed, picked up a book, and read about Russia.

'On their arrival in Naples they were greeted by the tableau of a wedding. Red, gleaming, marionettes' roses crowded about a bride negroid from the summer under her white veils. She held a little bouquet of roses herself and with her gait, a singular slow gait, her head turned like a doll's to either side for attention, in her giving smile Keats perceived death.'

I perceived nothing outside the chip shop. I'd tried to escape this domain so many times but my attempts always floundered. In my black leather jacket, another of my parents' indulgences towards me, I stared.

'The path to Rome was linked by skeletons hanging from trees and by the straining skeletons of horses. The young poet stared ahead, still mesmerized by the look in the bride's face.'

Would you take me out of my mesmerization Eugene? Could you change my life? Could you impart a little of what you have learned from Russian literature? In class I asked stupid questions. The priest continued.

'Entering Rome through the Lantern Gate, Joseph Severn pointed out an old cardinal in scarlet peeping out of a rickshaw, white whiskers drooping on him. Young girls purveyed their wares of white mice on trays strapped round the neck. Boys, celestial faced, entertained with guitar picking. John Keats had arrived at the Mecca, the metropolis of life and found himself surrounded by the pervasive and stenching chill of death. Sitting upright in the carriage he was aware of his poem still pushing, the beginnings of it, a birth. In Rome it was a green thing, his poem. With a brother he climbed again through boughs. A carriage pulled up outside a hotel on the Piazza di Spagna.'

Eugene turned about. I thought he was turning towards me. He was checking the clouds piled even higher outside.

'Upstairs in the hotel lived a young Irishman who kept them awake at nights with the songs of Ireland. But Keats and his friend were lulled by these songs.'

The songs of Ireland! What rubbish. The mind was wandering again; the inflammation of nasturtiums throwing up shapes. A young Irishman wandered through Rome, treading on Keats' grave, reeling drunkenly down alleys of white, his mind filled with the long, black, supine, abandoned boots of the Irish Brigade or merely by the cinema posters, portraying brat faced boys on motorcycles, which haunted Rome at that time.

'Rome was far from England. In bed in a small hotel John Keats remembered the winter blossom creeping along a sloping lane in Hampstead, his lover's breasts.'

Spidery, white knuckles tightened. A variety of minds envisaged the nipples of Keats' love, pink and voluminous.

'There was still in the middle of illness opportunity for walks. With the aid of his companion John Keats circulated in Rome. In the

82

Borghese Gardens he caught sight of a princess who'd posed half-naked for a notorious statue. Again there was the rapture, the abandon, the baby-like impotence of first love.'

A gallery of nipples appeared before my eyes, those of young girls I'd either seduced or became fatigued by in the act of seducing.

'At Christmas the young Irishman entertained them with stories and songs, Keats, sitting up, blanketed, as they sipped on mulled wine spiced with cinnamon and nutmeg.'

Eugene turned again. This time I thought I caught his eye. Today I would ask him home.

'January in Rome is the worst time, no particular season, no particular grasping point. Summer, winter, spring, autumn in turn. The young poet screamed. Illness had made him a little old lady, a gnome-like skeleton at times. Illness had taken the loveliness and the youth he had sung about so often. Retching, throwing up bile, blood and something beyond bile and blood, something purple, evil, squalid, he reached a quivering hand for the phials of poison he'd smuggled with him. But to no avail. Joseph Severn held them back. Birds gathered on fences for southern flight. Scarecrows shook in fields of corn before thunder. The landscape of death felt oddly like home. But it was not the closeness to death which caused him most anguish, but the fact that as yet he did not have his poem. John Keats wandered. He wandered past the wastes, the barrenness, the midnight hours of creativity, the undulating hours when you try, you punish yourself but nothing will ever come again, the life of words is dead for you. Joseph Severn held the young poet. He was a silken object now, shaking. One night a terrific storm blew up as only Rome knows how to blow up these storms. It was John Keats' worst night. He screamed, raved; he crossed the frontiers of Hell and then hesitated for he knew that art, like a storm, is a struggle and if you stay with it it will give forth. Suddenly in a flash of lightning the young man saw his last poem. He saw that death itself would be his last poem. By dying he'd be leaving the impression of life on his poetry and thereby transcending art for ever and becoming part of life. Girls from the mountains called about their cheeses in the square outside. Rainbows perched over pools of water. John Keats died.'

I remembered Alan as I'd imagined him in that garden on my first confrontation with Eugene and Cherine, Alan, the grandiose artist, and how subsequently the mood had shifted, the band had started up and Alan had danced with my mother, she in a blue dress, his awkward attempt to transcend art.

'John Keats was buried in early morning as only then could

Protestants be buried in Rome. It was a grey morning. Severe, Protestant faces looked on. A girl, fresh and distinctive faced among them, threw a first sprig of almond blossom.'

Boys in blue and white striped jerseys squelched over runny fields in a game of hurling as Eugene and I made our way to my house. A flotsam of geese, hunched and protesting, greeted us. My mother had not been up to feeding them too well of late. A ladder led to my room. Eugene, shoulders drooping, seated himself on the bed, under a triad of cut-outs, Marianne Faithfull, Gerry and the Pacemakers, Barry McGuire. I took up a guitar my parents had bought for me the previous Christmas and strummed into a song I'd composed about little girls disappearing into the Blackwoods for ever.

'Little girls, little girls, gone to pick berries.'

Eugene was visibly unimpressed. In my white jersey I waited. The guitar lay, a graven object. The Dublin train shot by, distantly, shaking a few nearby sensitive and spring-awakened birch trees. That evening at the window of his main street home Eugene pulled back a curtain and spied a girl strolling through the mist, black stockings under her short coat and a long fluorescent pink chiffon scarf protruding at her neck. Cherine Finnerty was home.

[8]

Eugene escaped that spring. With a volume of Russian literature under his arm he disappeared to the prom in the afternoons after school, parking himself on a scarlet bench under a thick and unruly clump of ivy, his auburn hair falling in a mass on the freckles of his forehead as he got lost in his book. Little old ladies in black admired his fawn tweed jacket. Otherwise there were no intruders. The ladies spent most of their time surveying a civil war ruin beyond the rivulet, or hesitating over a shining and vagarious blackbird before moving on. One day a white blob appeared in the distance. This mysterious blob grew larger, approached. Cherine Finnerty seated herself next to Eugene, immersed herself in her rival work of Russian literature and with the weeks – as little old ladies in black were quick to notice – assiduously moved herself closer to Eugene until their literary interchanges took place at such an intimate distance that the names, the authoritative invocations were inextricably infused with whatever brand of cheap perfume Cherine happened to be wearing that day.

In 1916 when Pearse and Connolly called the men of Ireland to arms four young men from the west answered their call. Let's say they were Peader, Oisín, Sean-Óg and Maolhachlainn. They came from the extreme west of Ireland, a place of covert blue bays, of dilapidated boats, of fishing, of tilling black and contrary soil. They were uniquely happy with their home – a place where Gaelic was spoken – but they felt it to be their primordial, their familial duty to fight for Ireland. They wielded sticks much as they might the flesh of hurling sticks – as if they would have an effect on the British empire by battering on the head an unsuspecting R.I.C. man. It was a fine, blue morning they set out. Oisín had packed herring sandwiches – herring suffocating and moistened in chunks of brown bread. Bottles stuck like hares' ears out of pockets. Maolhachlainn lagged behind. He admired the bluebells along the laneways of Connemara. 'We'll never get there,' Peader, the oldest, declared, as if they were intending to go to a donkey race. They passed little chapels, pubs outside which old men looked them up and down without batting an eyelid. They were travelling to fight for Ireland all right. The names on pub doors were in Gaelic. They were still in Connemara. Once their ancestors had ploughed west before Cromwell's men, the families, the tains of Drogheda, of Arklow. They'd dragged onwards laden with shining tables and with jewellery. Now these lads were retracing their steps. They were intent on ousting the Saxon – that very week if need be! An old lady pulled her black shawl about her and grinned. In Carraroe the four young men stopped on the first night and drank in Concubhur's pub near the ocean.

Galway city was full of hustle and bustle, tinkers, calves, ponies and traps, businessmen elders in bowler hats, the ever present R.I.C., and the army on the prowl, eyes darting from under helmets often polished. A mouse scurried out from underneath a stack of oatmeal. Was he a revolutionary? A soldier's eyes dashed. The boys sauntered proudly through Galway. They had their shirts off. 'We'll be back to celebrate in the Great Southern,' they said. Sean-Óg wished to go to the Claddagh to visit an aunt but the others pulled him on. They left the city of the tribes, which kow-towed in every direction to Britain, and moved on; soon Galway city, if they had their way, would change, soon ladies there could not afford to be so snooty of the nature of Connemara. Ireland would change. It would be a country for the poor.

85

There was little sign of revolution or the activity of revolution on the roads of County Galway. Old women went by in carts, donkeys slumberously dragging them. Long pipes in their mouth, the boys wanted to shout to these ancients that there was a revolution, to wake up. They slept in a field. Oisín sang 'Róisín Dubh', a song about Mother Ireland raising herself to wakefulness, and Peader described a film he'd seen in the cinema in Galway. He was the only one to have seen a film and it seemed a miracle to them all; 'God be praised,' one of them attested, and another added that he heard that Hollywood was the new Sodom and Gomorrah and would be devoured by flames very shortly. And that made another one of them drone on about Lot's wife. 'You know I feel sympathy with her. The one who looks back.'

Their country was a blue one in history; full of legends, the Spanish came and the Cromwellians. Galway city was the jewel of Galway; Oisín, the one most versed in history, garbled little tales about Galway city, about the mayors, the earls, how the townspeople had gathered so many times of revolution but how money had always held sway. They remembered their own morning passing through Galway city, donkeys bearing sea-weed by the sand, and men fishing for salmon, Galway city much as it would have been when their people came from the east. In Loughrea they stopped on the Green. Here the Cromwellians had meted out small tracts of land to the westward-going Irish in the seventeenth century.

You have taken the East from me;
You have taken the West from me;
You have taken what is before me and what is behind me;
And my fear is great that you have taken God from me!

In Kilreekill, outside a pub, a girl sang a song translated from the Gaelic. The boys raised their pints of beer to her. The war was coming closer but now it seemed a cataclysm more than a war, a conflict between Cromwellians and Spaniards, opposing shadows over the history of this county. They could not exactly decipher their own thoughts, but they were aware, half-aware, as they headed east again that history has its own victims; and Cromwellians can be as deceived as anyone else. After all Cromwell understood the sacking of Drogheda to be the will of God.

Now they were entering alien territory. The abodes more sedate, the curling smoke more suspicious. Here Ireland merged with England. Here the Irish had long ago given in. The men from the west felt like apes, felt inferior, unattractive, cumbersome. Their steps dragged – dinosaur steps. But they were determined they'd reach Dublin and amend history. At this stage each and everyone of them had the notion of turning back; hurling, dancing, drinking seemed singularly more attractive than rebellion making. They valued their arms, their legs; they wanted to do a reel again. They remembered the words of the priest in the slate grey chapel at home. 'Blessed are the peacemakers: for they shall be called the children of God.' A donkey looked at them forlornly. In unison they had the imagination to turn back but tremulously they forged forward. Soon it would be Athlone, the great bridge, the bloodied stone, the true marking point between east and west of Ireland, the irrevocable; they began saying prayers, the prayers of the dying. Yes, they were going to fight for Ireland. They'd surely be killed.

But fate stepped in before these boys could be killed; in the town where Eugene, Cherine and I lived fifty years later, these boys met, in sleeping on the fair Green, a band of tinkers, and these they joined in celebrations, dancing, singing, drinking, story-telling beside a bonfire. The celebrations went on for a week and by that time the revolution was over in Ireland. The boys, the four would-be heroes, swayed home – drunk.

Fifty years later, during the preparations for the fiftieth anniversary of the 1916 revolution, it would be interesting to speculate as to the subsequent biographies of these four boys. Sean-Óg, the youngest, was in San Francisco. He owned a furniture removal business there. He forever wore an emerald curio. He bawled at his employees, he waveringly genuflected to priests. Ólsin was a retired school-teacher in the Bronx. Most of his stories to black and Puerto Rican school children had been about the heroic deeds of the 1916 revolution. Maolhachlainn was dead in a cemetery in Halifax, prayed over by a wife from near the Shannon, County Offaly, and Peader, the oldest, was in the local mental hospital. He'd come back to this town, not a victorious hero, but described as insane. Fifty years on, fifty years of loneliness, celibacy, sisters leaving, masturbation in a small cottage by the sea, herring ultimately speaking to him, in shoals, fifty years of revolution. Peader looked from behind iron bars and remembered leaping in a reel beside a raging bonfire Easter week 1916.

As the town prepared for the celebrations all eyes were on a school-teacher who'd been writing a pageant for the previous five years, a pageant uniting nearly every imaginable episode of Irish history but, some weeks before Easter 1966, when the dignitaries of the town were seeking the belated manuscript to perform some of it at least, he announced, this pale and jittery man, that the playscript had metamorphosed into a poem, a poem about everything, Cúchulainn, the Normans, Queen Elizabeth, Hugh O'Neill, Cromwell, Wolfe Tone, 'the whole shagging lot' as a local councillor ranted. The poem would be finished by Easter 2016 according to someone else, so a literary form of celebration was abandoned; one knew that in a garret in town, by lamplight, Irish history was being illumined for the millionth time, scarlet cloaks swishing, pikes embattling and Mother Ireland lifting her skirts to urinate before yet another defeat. Children had waited in vain for roles as gallóglach, the medieval vagrant Irish soldiers, so instead it was uniformly agreed there'd merely be a parade.

Coming up to the commemoration ceremonies Mrs. Houlihan, the head of the urban council, was beset by strange dreams which she failed to confess. She dreamt she was sleeping with some of the 1916 heroes, turning with them. James Connolly's chest was brandished with hair. Patrick Pearse was pale, venial even in nakedness. Mrs. Houlihan traipsed in her pale blue nightdress to the window, desiring on that spot to be engulfed in a panoramic Irish flag. No such luck. She had to live with this charge of eroticism in her. A big woman, her arms pale and thick, she looked herself as if she was waiting to overpower a man. But big, unwieldy or not, there'd been a time she'd lain with a young lad in a bed of marigolds on the Blasket Islands; a girl from Dublin she'd gone to improve her Irish. Now look at her – in middle-age – by orange street lights in a small town reliving, being turbulent with her girlhood sexuality. A lifetime separated her from a young lad on the Blasket Islands and a heart heavily pounding now.

Mother Ireland – that lady of many disguises – took to the streets that Easter. Old men, suits hanging from them as from coat hangers. Girl-guides, chewy, blank faced, emerald girl-guides. A few ragged members of the Legion of Mary in blue and white.

In the square from a platform Mrs. Houlihan – herself often called Cathleen after Cathleen ni Houlihan, one of the pseudonyms for Mother Ireland – made a speech. 'Patrick Pearse loved purity. There was purity on his face and on his soul . . .' A fat member of the brass band made an irregular and premature sound into a trombone. The Irish flag limply kissed the Vatican flag. Rain threatened. Boys, the refuse of town, stared, blanker than anybody, from the bank corner. People dispersed as the skies totally blackened and the rain came, punishing chocolate paper and cigarette papers alike. In the mental hospital they conducted their own celebrations. Peader, in a paper hat, danced close to a mongoloid girl in a waltz, the band of the mental hospital later starting up a rousing version of 'Roddy McCordy' which brought tears to one woman's eyes and sent three hefty Connemara men into rebellion against male nurses.

From the top of a hill I watched. Smoke curled flaccidly from my father's factory. Word was out. The factory was on the wane. My father, reacting at last to my mother's affairs, had taken to drink. Pudgy bottles of whiskey pouted under a portrait of the local bishop, proudly attesting to his purple paunch. Women, Easter lilies still clinging to their fat bosoms, looked to the sky as if for confirmation. To coincide with the fiftieth anniversary of the 1916 Revolution the small bit of the town's prosperity had temporarily had its day.

Eileen Carmody took to the Galway road as often she'd done before. Today she was more agitated than before. It was as if bodies were her only religion, all that made sense to her, flesh, nipples, genitals. 'I want to fuck, fuck, fuck.' By now she was a caricature. Even a goose looked at her with aplomb. What was it about the 1916 anniversary celebrations that triggered off in her anger, regret; she did not want to be herself any more, she wanted to be different, transcend her needs. Presidents might stream words of national congratulations, bishops might spray with holy water but the fact remained; she'd been rejected by this country and felt only her body to be real, her body thrown against other bodies, like the stones of stone walls thrown upon one another. The nights of weeks she did not make love were nights filled with desire; sexuality took place in her like an overpowering battle. It was her language but it was wearing her away. In short, she knew herself today to be a laughing stock. Eileen Carmody stopped on the road to talk to a young lad. He worked some of the time on a farm, some of the time on the roads. He had scintillating dark eyes. He wore a white shirt. This boy did not know her reputation. He spoke to her cordially – as to a stranger. On her rather strange inquiry he added to autobiographical details already given; he wanted to go to England, to travel. He had a widower father. They lived on a small farm. The boy liked the cinema. Gary Cooper was his favourite actor. And hers? O God save us, she laughed, ages since she'd been to a film. George Sanders she mentioned regally as if that would tell something good about her. 'You've got a bit of an English accent,' the boy observed. She told him she'd lived in England for a while. 'Would you like a cigarette?' she asked. They deserted the road for a familiar dry patch beside heather in the bog to smoke. The boy smoked – arduously. 'You look a bit lonely to me.' A hearse passed. The boy magically reached out his hand to suggest a cannon ball his father had discovered in the earth –

the boy's palm outstretched as if the cannon ball had been a big black olive. Eileen Carmody walked home. She'd not made love. She'd never make love to anyone again – except her husband. Someone had treated her like a human being today.

My mother shrouded my father's bald pate in a kitchen where the light had not been turned on. I intruded. I made a hurried exit. But the night no longer wanted me, the main street. I'd noticed Eugene's serenity of late. One afternoon I followed him. History came with me as I approached him and Cherine, the history of Ireland and familial history – Alan's novel. I asked friendship of them and they gave it to me.

'1916,' Martin Finnerty muttered. Martin Finnerty had passed the 1916 anniversary celebrations in his sitting-room beside the cemetery. A picture of the pope there; his wife, in youth. Plastic flowers, heavily floral yellow ochre wallpaper. Balls with snow in them in the glass case, porcelain, foot poised ballerinas on top of it. His deaf and dumb daughter succoured him with biscuits and steaming tea. Martin Finnerty took the 1916 commemoration ceremonies as an opportunity to browse over his life; to celebrate his own fifty odd years and to give himself the pleasure of feeling exalted. These days, a patriarch, he sojourned in the sitting-room, the memory of nine children, two of them twins, often diffused into a conversation with his wife, a letter on headed notepaper.

22 April 1966

Dearest Lilian,

They've been celebrating 1916. I think all the celebrations have come to an end now. It feels like that. I miss you, sweetheart. The town's changed since you've been around. The children don't write anymore. I'm alone – almost. The dead come in every day. Last week Catherine Hanratty died. You know the one who always hit little boys with newspapers and claimed she was related to a papal count. Sometimes it feels as if everyone in the town has died. There's a terrible silence now. That silence never seems to break. There are things still I want to talk to you about, nights which I feel are still going on. Often I walk in the cemetery, look at your grave and see a young couple ballroom dancing. But history became real didn't it, the Cromwells, the Oliver Plunketts became the gas chambers of Auschwitz. We danced together into the gas chambers. We were in love but there's no room for love now, Lilian, the world no longer needs love. The children are either perverted or silent. A ripple comes from somewhere – your grave. It's our song again, our dance; will you take the floor Lilian? Will you dance with me? Will you cure the ache, the pain, the loneliness of these days? There, the mental hospital windows are lighting up. Good night Lily, sweetheart, God bless . . .

His deaf and dumb daughter entered with tea.

Martin had seen this town become rainier, hearts bleaker all right; no one spoke to one another any more so he talked to the dead. He talked to National school-teachers and seamstresses, he talked to rich and poor. They could not talk back.

The 1916 celebrations came and went; the flags were unfurled and the speeches made. Martin Finnerty strolled into the cemetery one evening and encountered the first real bit of spring in the sky.

Mrs. McDermott walked over wet, gnashed Easter lilies. She was taking her routine evening walk. Life was lonely for Mrs. Mc-Dermott. Sometimes she went to Dublin to stay with her daughter. She'd stayed there that Easter. The whole city was celebrating 1916. You could hardly get to Mass. They observed the Easter military parade in Dublin. Cardinals, priests out in great numbers. Military tanks floated by. Regiments of boy-scouts lapsed onwards, the scarf of each regiment a different colour. The Legion of Mary rather absent-mindedly appeared at this parade too. In her daughter's house Mrs. McDermott perused *The Irish Catholic*. She read everything about 1916 that was to be known. 1916 was the property of God now, the angels, the missionary Irish saints. In fact it was Catholicism itself. Spring came to the mountains. Mrs. McDermott described the annual traders' dinner-dance at home to her daughter, the dress she herself had worn, black. Middle-aged now, Mrs. McDermott was still lovelier than her daughter. Easter 1966 she thought – very, very briefly – of a young man who'd gone out to fight for Spain whom she used to meet in an ice-cream parlour in Dublin once. The rain fell on the chocolate papers, the sweet papers, the discarded paper Easter lilies of Dublin too.

In Almeria once a young Irishman fired by the spirit of 1916 browsed among the conflagration of flowers.

'Mammy, how's Eugene?'

Familiar question.

This evening Mrs. McDermott answered that question – more fully and to herself. Eugene was strange, misbegotten, Eugene was reminiscent of so many things alien, upsetting and even venomous to her. A woman passed the time of evening to her. Mrs. McDermott nodded in her direction. This evening, in the aftermath of 1916 celebrations,

91

Eugene's features merged into the face of her oldest, dead sister, a sister in fact by another marriage, the only child of her father's first marriage which ended in the death of his wife. Perhaps that was what explained the separateness, the slight estrangement from their reality – the reality of the farm, of the Shannon – of her sister. In an evening in April, Mrs. McDermott imagined her sister again by the Shannon as she had been the day of Mrs. McDermott's wedding, a woman walking and her brown eyes becoming her son's eyes. Children are conceived at strange moments. Despite the complexity of her earlier thoughts during her ritual private rosary that night, her husband out drinking, her daughter in Dublin, her son at his homework, Mrs. McDermott demolished all intricacy and prayed for the umpteenth time that her son Eugene would make a Jesuit.

'The hour of remembrance had drawn close again . . .' In this town once lived a Russian woman. She'd left Russia some time around the Russian revolution and she'd married a local doctor. In her garden had been an oak tree, fuschia in summer, yellow broom in spring. This woman, if you believed some, had killed herself for want of something better to do. She'd left a son, cats, mice, a husband. The husband had left town. Other people lived in her house but still her wine, her music parties in a room of dark timber swooned in the memory. Because of her or maybe because of a surfeit of Russian literature Cherine – after she finished detailing her first mini-skirt, a red tartan one, or the London buses and post office boxes, also red – began, in white, on the rivulet bank because it was fine now, us two sitting, to lecture on Russian writers. There she was, a stodgy professor against the sky. Little old ladies in black often stopped by the wire beside the trees for a snippet of information.

Looking back it is a room. There is an invocation of postcards in this room. Claudette Colbert clambers alongside an old, white haired Russian. Alan types. Sometimes, either in peace or desperation, he deserts his typewriter and, as it is fine and early summer, takes a walk along the Bull Wall. In a men's changing hut, half open to the sky, he enthrones himself on a bench. Old men turn their white, rouge blotched backsides to him. The towel falls off a young man. Alan's head reclines against graffiti concerning Hitler, his eyes close and as old men murmer and chatter about the temperature of the sea, the reported number of ships sunk the previous night, Alan sees a schoolroom in Athlone, a teacher, looming, declaring with a stick 'Cissy Mulvanney' and later in a boys' lavatory as the other boys urinate Alan enfolding his penis for fear it would be seen because of its size.

'There are moments which unite past and future,' a Frenchwoman said to me, 'but are most perfectly themselves.' Such a moment was the early weeks of summer 1966 for Eugene, Cherine and myself.

Years later Cherine, a young business woman, her name over a boutique on the main street, would stroll in early morning to the old house, stand on the veranda, look to the harvest fields and wonder where she had gone, a girl in a white dress lecturing on Russian poets.

Eugene, a young social worker in blue denim, would walk also early one morning, into a community centre in Belfast where he was working with Catholic and Protestant young people for a few weeks before leaving Ireland. Of late his youngsters would have become obsessed with American-type psychiatry, improvising wild therapy sessions. Today a boy, seventeen, Catholic, in blue, would rise and very soon everyone would realize he was not improvising. This was for real. 'They say you need God, religion, politics, sex, friends,' he'd announce, 'Well they're lying.' He'd turn about. 'I was in jail. There was no God, religion, politics, sex, friends there. They all desert you.' A girl would shift uneasily in her seat. 'Friends even.' He'd confront Eugene again, very directly and whisper in a winsome Belfast accent. 'It's just yourself isn't it. All you've got is yourself.' With that he'd leave. People would look to Eugene to see how they should react but he'd just stare after the boy, recalling . . .

I, a soldier, leaning on an armalite outside a school in which children had until recently chanted 'Daily, Daily oing to Maιy', would look to the hills and wonder about the dichotomy of it, harvest in the hills, fear, death, desperation in the city.

'There are moments in life which bring everything together,' the Frenchwoman stated, 'the past, future, other people.' Such moments were the weeks of early summer 1966.

Looking back it is a room. Alan types in this room. His white shirt sticks to his baby skin. He types on against a time of war in the outside world and in his home country the violation of dissent. He types on beside a window which touches green leaves and in a room which holds books, postcards. He knows wherever he goes he will bring the values of this room, books, postcards, outside green leaves. No one interrupts him today. Near Athlone the orange lily pods would be leaping up on the lakes and, in the imagination, a young couple on horseback would saunter beside these lakes, accompanied by two boys, a bishop. For the moment they are safe. Alan types on and we hear his typing in the early weeks of summer 1966.

93

One day, standing, us two sitting as usual, Cherine pointed to swans flying over. There was no forgetting. I took books from the library and in my darkened attic room, foliage pressing against the window, I read.

In the seventeenth century in England, particularly during the civil war in England and the rebellion in Ireland, people took to the roads of England. At first these people were nameless, unnoticed, an ongoing of the phenomenon which had been happening since the end of the previous century, whole populations on the move, the cities emptied and the fens, the forests occupied. But these human beings were different. They smiled. The smiles were ungainly but always broad. Diggers, Ranters, Levellers, Seekers, Anabaptists they were called. The names got confused as did the differentiations between one group and another. But one thing was certain. Some people had either drunk too much or had seen history in a light it had never been seen in before. The land was the people's they declared, the risen Christ was on the move, he was a ragamuffin, a gypsy, he was human, he was sexual. The young man, passing your window, a red scarf around his neck, smiled and invited you to follow. New songs were heard, scandals of a totally different nature to scandals harbingered before. Naked people stood en masse and greeted the sun. New airs whisked by your window, new lilts. In a time of war there was hope, renaissance in the air even. A lad sat in Newbury playing a tin whistle as the battle raged. The scandal intensified, eclipsed the execution of kings, even when men actually lay down their arms. On their way to Ireland some among the New Model Army refused to fight. The same year the Diggers' leader Robert Lockier was buried, his body carted in a shower of rosemary tainted by blood. Soon he became a song. Soon the whole movement, the inflammation of red scarves against the sun, became a song. But songs live, they turn and turn again and are remembered.

About the same time in Ireland, if you were to believe stories picked up by Alan Mulvanney in Roscommon, a young man and a young woman set out to preach peace. Ireland was different to England. Crosses held their one arm into the mists. Convents were ramshackle, hills gaping, nuns, priests on the move, populations cannibalistic, bishops flying in gold through the cannibalism. The legends, the myths of centuries were over – *Insula sanctorum et doctorum* – the friars no longer flitted off to Jerusalem to kiss relics, nuns no longer gathered the honey, masks on their faces. God had not come to roll back the sea as he had done to the Israelites. Eyes stared, blackened like bad potatoes. In this landscape a young man and woman on a white horse, two boys, a Protestant bishop slowly moved. They moved into our century because such are legends and songs; they keep going. A white horse swayed into our vision via a novel by Alan Mulvanney, and Lorcan and Eleanor spoke of nuclear weapons, of a world about to be destroyed. Or so the parable seems tonight; in an army barracks in Belfast, a city where the dead are found in sewers, where old tramps are hacked to death by butchers' knives, where pregnant girls are beaten to death by bricks.

'It is to be ever remembered how Our Saviour, out of the abundance of His mercy, hath about Our lady's day in the lent last, freed and cleared this town and all its inhabitants thereof from the said sickness, so as they have returned to their own dwellings, and ever since do inhabit them with as much security as ever before.' It is winter and Lorcan and Eleanor hide in Galway in the house in Pludd Street, their mission over, corpses and gargantuan rats in the streets about them but inside a candle mirthfully melts into a gnome-like shape. Fiction passes into life, and in those moments in early summer 1966 Alan's novel seemed real life again.

Cherine's cousin, Sabina Finnerty, left Ireland for Hollywood in 1947. Unlike Cherine's father's part of the family, she did not grow up in Flea Lane but further out, nearer the bogs. Bog cotton threaded and entangled her childhood. Sabina would rob donkey boys – the boys who beat donkeys on with a stick in one hand and rode a bicycle with another – bicycles to take herself into town where she could dangle like a wraith outside the cinema. It was the 1930s. The unemployed feasted on pigeon sandwiches – one family was known to do it! – on the fair Green. Greta Garbo, Jean Harlow, Clark Gable arrived in buckets in a long, ricochetted van. Sabina rarely had the money to go to the pictures. She observed a ritual, hands behind her back, of paying respect to glamour. 'Sabina, Sabina,' her rough people cackled. She made no answer. She was already off to the far city. She'd become the Greta Garbo of Ireland. Boys fingered her and she looked as if she didn't feel it. 'The patron saint of pinkeens,' someone called her, thinking of pinkeens issuing around the sewer pipe in the river. Sabina prayed to 'Our Lady of Hollywood', imagining a virgin, not unlike herself, elevated from the grime of a town such as this and standing over Hollywood, hands outstretched and an aureole of neon about her head. Sabina became Madonna-like, waif-like in obeisance to this image. The trip to Hollywood began outside the cinema on the main street.

Mind you, the first stages were hard; milking a contrary, garrulous cow, cycling a wilting, brown bicycle, giving your body for boys' pleasure because you knew that's what had to be done. Only her uncle Martin, just a few years older than herself, understood. He told her she had the face of Greta Garbo in *Queen Christina*.

During the war Sabina was in London. She did not heed air raid sirens because she knew she had a destiny. Hands behind her back she walked among the rubble. Always, no matter where she went, to Hollywood, Hawaii, Hindustan, she'd carry with her geese, a bog, the mournful sky. Sabina, not getting much luck in making a start in the cinema industry briefly returned to Ireland. She worked in a hotel in Belfast where Martin's wife had once worked; her application to her work deteriorated. In a blue coat she knew it was Hollywood or nothing. The Statue of Liberty was calling. To hell with the king of England. When she told her mother she was off, her mother threw a fit. 'You'll stay and marry a decent man.' Sabina ran away to Liverpool with money robbed from a local rich farmer she'd slept with – he'd kept it hidden under the floorboards – and she bought a ticket for New York. The boat stopped at Cobh. Her whole family was there to try to get her off but the distance between the boat and shore would be Sabina's distance for ever from her home, from the place among the fields you had to sleep with a rich farmer to get anywhere. Tinkers were there at the port at Cobh, ponies and carts, ponies and traps. Her mother screamed, 'May you die on the way.' Sabina was soon out on the open Atlantic.

In New York, she lived in East 43rd Street. She travailed in an Irish bar under the tricolour. She knew again she had to be on her way. She bought a Greyhound bus ticket with her earnings and headed west. A great-uncle lived in Philadelphia and she stopped with him briefly and looked at old photographs, the tinkers of Ireland, their caravans. Off she was again.

Sitting back on the bus to Pittsburgh, the languid, acquiline, black-haired girl heard Mennonites sing their songs of salvation. In a bus station in the mid-west, her curls on her shoulders, a cup at her lips, she felt the first dash in her dreams of being a star. She desired domesticity. Matthew was the man in her life for a while. Forty-two. She encountered him in another bus station. She went to his farm, a hillside in Iowa State, and lived a winter with him. The American flag chilled over the corn fields. The sunsets became louder, more eloquent. Pumpkins lined under the American flag. At Thanksgiving over cornish hens Sabina thought of her own little town in Ireland where the prospect of someone ever imagining thanksgiving was dim.

In the evenings, in Matthew's trailer, she'd ride off to a pub. Eventually the country and western music of the juke-box spoke to her too directly of travel and roads. She arranged to meet a truck-driver in this pub one night and, without telling Matthew, took her case and in a long coat disappeared out the back door of the pub. The truck-driver brought her as far as Omaha. From there she picked up the bus again, crossed the Rockies, stayed briefly with Madeleine, a woman who had porcelain swans in the window. Madeleine, in her home in the Rockies, an old lady, white wisps of hair over her forehead, in the garden in the spring afternoons, reminded Sabina of Ireland. In 1948 with her case Sabina stepped out of a car into orange light. She had arrived on Hollywood Boulevard.

In early May 1966, Cherine dreamt of Sabina. She dreamt she was Sabina stepping out of that car, looking around in the unpeopled orange light, entering a pub Sabina had often mentioned in her letters, Musso Frank's, there by the counter a young man turning in her direction whom she at first thought to be Montgomery Clift but whose features as they confronted her became those of Alan Mulvanney, the young man I'd often spoken of.

Mrs. McDermott's oldest sister, Eugene's aunt, was born in a different part of Ireland to the other members of her family. Meath. She only moved to the Shannon when her mother died and her father married again. There'd always been that bit of difference between her and her brother and sisters, not just age, another part of Ireland, a more solemn one. She left Ireland in 1929 to follow a friend to Germany. She stayed only briefly, returning to England, losing herself in a variety of suitable occupations, but something stayed in her eyes, something that was akin to the landscape of her earliest childhood, to the country of Germany, a vague, unnameable turbulence in the air, in the boulevards, a dusk in crowded trams that made you think of the disquiet of May lilac in Meath, garden roofs falling in on nettles, the history of Protestantism and Protestantism as it affected this area, punishing it. She returned to Germany, pursuing a thread. Germany returned her to childhood -- 'True friendship never fades away Although the times may alter; And thoughts of thee but pass away Each morrow to be greater' – to cemeteries on hillsides where she was bewildered by glass domes reflecting her, to ruins by pacific turns in the river, to echoing screams in the hallways of Protestants, Catholic servant girls having fallen down the stairs years ago. Germany more than anything reminded her of the cornfields of Meath, cornfields always bristling with the shadow of guilt. In

Germany she returned to the source of her Catholicism, a dark source. There were shadows on every face, the shadows of her childhood Meath. Maybe she'd gone looking for her dead, nearly Victorian mother. She ambled on streets. She stopped in chapels to pray before the Sacred Heart. A crimson flame flickered uneasily. A woman from Skerries spoke in the evening, droned 'Long ago . . .' The stories of Ireland. Even in Hitler's Germany. Eugene's aunt got a job, minding children. It was a big house, in the centre of Berlin. Lace curtains buffeted. She taught the children to pray. That would be her great achievement in life – to tutor children in how perfectly to join their hands together. Germany for these months, these weeks, was Ireland. She tried to decipher the meaning of her thoughts. She could not. They escaped – into the country. By lakes. Bavaria threw its cooling breeze on them. The Hitler Youth movement jumped about with spouting bottles of beer. She sang a song for them. They applauded it. 'Danny Boy.' 'Mein Gott, es ist genau wie ein deutsches Lied.' Danny Boy had blond hair. She wanted to go further, decipher an image. Was it history or childhood? In Bucharest, on holiday, in a brown suit, in a café, late summer, she reclined, marigolds in a thick bunch on a shelf, the proprietor silently leaning on the counter in a blue, white-speckled smock, Eugene's aunt's hand just about on a glass of white wine. This was perfection, childhood. They were just about to sweep the leaves outside. No matter what happened, death, any kind of abortion, she had found it: these moments in Bucharest, peace. Her children grew a little. The woman of the house trusted her Catholicism with all its intricacies. Eugene's aunt imparted prayer. But her own prayer deep inside was for mankind. You felt that shadow from childhood but it absorbed humanity. One day the Hitler Youth threw old age pensioners out of the top story of a Jewish hospital onto the pavement in front of her. An old man's head at her shoe, blood. 'Mary Mother of God . . .' The concentration camps dotted the map of Germany like a constellation of stars. The hand of a lovely Jewish girl, thinking of becoming a convert, was arrested in mid flight . . . she'd been writing a poem about the Queen of Heaven. The woman of the house croaked her prayers. There was silence in Germany. Silence in the chapels. You noticed fewer graceful faces on the streets. The beauty of girls' features was ebbing. All the Jewish girls were gone. The church was silent, even the Sacred Heart was silent. Trains split across Germany. Eugene's aunt took one. She was reminded of a history lesson at school: the Irish going west. She wanted to stay and extend Irish friendship to a Jewish population, but fear took her away and the shadow of those atrocities she'd seen. It was spring in the forests. In France she stopped, made a detour to Chartres, a cathedral, a building she'd heard to be perfect, lit a long, twig-like candle before the gold, majestic, ornamental Our Lady of Chartres and prayed for the fate of conscience.

Early in May 1966, Eugene, her nephew, took up a card she'd sent from that trip to Chartres, reading simply: 'Remembering you in my prayers'; and for some reason, Chartres being synonymous with the manifestation of creativity in a time of peril, survival against bombs, Eugene thought of a young man I'd often spoken of, Alan Mulvanney.

As May reached its height, little boys in white elevating their hands in the arch gesture of prayer for their first holy communions, the laburnum and the red hawthorn brimming by the prom, Alan emerged from these things; the grave sensuality which made him see old men with sea-blue eyes among the lemon groves of Sevilla; the country that surrounded him and followed his footsteps. It was a country which lay halfway between 1916 and now, embraced by a fluttering Irish tricolour, the land of our parents, a country of covert corners of the gardens of big country houses, a country of Sunday walks in buttercup lanes on overshadowed afternoons. Someone was whistling a familiar tune in this country and it reached Alan's ears as he opened a door early one morning in May 1941 and headed out.

Alan hadn't begun writing his novel as yet. In fact he was only just beginning to think about it. In fact looking back, it would seem that it was today it hit him most forcibly – just as one saw a sparkling white shirt in flutin is' window. There were a lot of white shirts around in Dublin that month and white shirts made Alan think of childhood and first holy communion. Then it seemed you would achieve something in life. Like a sacrament. That's how the idea of realizing his novel came to him. He had to complete his childhood, holidays in the harvest slopes of Roscommon, his first poem.

There was a desperation about that urge today. What's the point of living if you don't do something? So a walk through Dublin became a re-examination of childhood, its crevices, a kind of memoir.

I am Alan Mulvanney. Born December 1919. To write a novel it seemed you first had to establish autobiography. Who you were, where you were from and why you were so bold as to dare to write.

Alan walked down Griffith Avenue to the Malahide Road. The Malahide Road led to Fairview and the sea. Although it was very fine today Alan wore his long coat as if he was shrouding himself against something. The coat was open, bedraggled after the winter. It looked competent to keep him warm on cold days though, but today looked crazy. Women smiled at him. He was an eegit. Catching sight of the blue sea on the turning of Griffith Avenue and the Malahide Road, Alan was brought back to Galway. In Athlone Galway was the first place. He didn't actually go there until he was an adolescent, but for Alan, a child, it was a source. Blue waters lapped on slimy grey stones. Spaniards stepped ashore. A whole life went on there. When Alan was a child he'd go to bed and a place like Galway would become real for him, Galway at the height of its prosperity. He liked to escape. But what was it he'd been escaping? Where were the muddled parts of childhood? He'd had brothers but they seemed unreal to him. A Christmas candle lighted again at a window in Athlone. A child pressed his nose to a window. An old man went by. Alan was taken back. That was the first stage in writing his novel. To return. Childhood dreams, a childhood world, ships on the sea and a poetry rising that calmed your fears.

There was always one particular fear in childhood. The fear of being hated. His brothers abandoned him. Some said he was neither boy nor girl. Alan sat on a wooden horse, alone.

'Alan.' Once his mother found him dressed as a girl. Alan was disgraced. The word whizzed among his brothers. He ran to a hill overlooking Athlone and looked down on a town that divided Ireland.

'Good morning. Is it Mr. Mulvanney?' A woman stopped him. She was a friend of his landlady. 'Isn't the war terrible? God is taking vengeance. People don't pray enough. But sure, as I said only yesterday, there are enough prayers in Dublin that should make up for the rest. If only God or his divine Mother would listen to me prayers about me varicose veins.'

What was the shame, the ignominy in childhood you could not return to? What was the shadow? Perhaps it was a good thing to acquaint yourself with shadows, to befriend them. In a backroom in Alan's mind was a child crying.

At school the teacher called him Cissy Mulvanney. The boys sneered at him. They said he had a small penis. That might have been a myth. Alan journeyed to an aunt and she helped him understand the world. It was the 1920s and there was a very good bakery in Athlone then. The Jewman owned it. In fact he wasn't Jewish but he went to symphony concerts in Dublin alone and people presumed he was. He was a foreigner. His mother distrusted the bread you got in this shop, but Alan, when he had money, bought bagels. There were the first history lessons at school. History was happening all around him. Protestant ladies committing suicide, cutting their throats, blood

100

dripping over floorboards, running into the street. Alan was brought to the zoo in Dublin.

What was this shadow in childhood? What was the meaning of it? Why think of it on a day like today? Alan had reached Fairview. The sea lay before him. He sat on a bench by a palm tree and presently a little girl joined him.

Out on that sea was the war. Alan, the student, stared at it and so did the little tinker girl before their conversation began. She told him she was an orphan; her mother and her father had died. She described her journeys and Alan saw it, all Ireland, exotic, magnificent, bewitching places, Donegal, Scellig Mhicil. The girl had been around. She'd seen the length and breadth of Ireland. Alan thought of the small points of Ireland he was familiar with, Galway, especially Roscommon. Roscommon had been his first panoramic experience of Ireland. You could smell the corn again, feel the flesh of a boy home from England sleeping alongside you, hear the milk being churned, hear a woman's voice dronc about dullaháns, banshees, pookas. You stood again in ungainly Protestant ruins. Here you felt shadows like you felt in your bedroom. You were arrested and troubled by something. What you didn't know.

Alice was the tinker girl's name, 'Miss Alice Ward,' she proudly announced. She asked Alan about Athlone. 'They're a rotten lot there', she pronounced. The young man and the girl parted, assuring one another they'd meet again.

In Roscommon you thought of all the misbegotten harvests of Ireland, but there was something else there, hope, fulfilment, young men home from England, laughter, perfume of cigarettes, red silk cravats, paper flowers. Some of these lads would be squashed by walls on building sites; some would die in war. In Roscommon they'd drunk porter and laughed. Alan continued on his way, down Annesley Bridge Road.

What Alan wanted to know on this walk was who he had been as a child and why the family he'd had. There was no sympathy for him in that family, no love. He'd always been discarded. An aunt called him a changeling. What had he come out of? So he made up relatives and ancestors, and saw Lorcan O'Mahony for the first time, wandering in Europe past wavering fires, searching for an image of a young man and memories of turbulent, warm fires.

> Upon the top of all his lofty crest
> A bunch of hares discoloured diversely
> With sprinkled pearl and gold full richly dressed

101

Did shake, and seemed to dance for jollity,
Like to an almond tree mounted high
On top of green Selinus all alone,
With blossom brave bedecked daintily;
Those tender locks do tremble everyone at every little
breath.

A school teacher quoted Spenser by mistake one day. A priest came to stay from Sevilla. In bed, alongside Alan, he made love to Alan. It would be Alan's last sexual experience with another person until he met my mother. Lying back in bed beside the priest he saw the orange trees and the purple Judas trees of Sevilla. When the priest had gone he'd been left with something, a legacy of scents, visions. Lorcan O'Mahony, an old man, was enthroned in a garden in Sevilla. The market place in Sevilla was busy. Queen Anne carried the skeleton sceptre in England.

At the Christian Brothers' school there were boys who spoke to him sympathetically, but they were always boys who were about to depart and go to England. Exile was the stuff of sympathy. Alan formed a relationship with the Shannon. By the Shannon he first envisaged a lover, girl, boy. He had sprouted up, a tall, lanky lad. There was no place for him in Athlone. On his first visits to Galway he noticed religion mix with the old rituals of celebrating summer. Eyes, honed out, looked through him. He was in Spain.

He'd written his first poem years before and now he wrote his first fiction. Sometimes he'd put down remarks. He was in love with other boys now. He'd sit in the rugby changing-room and watch buttocks. He wanted to make love to another boy. Cups were presented. He was alone.

Yes, at fifteen, he discovered he was alone. That was the operative word. In Dublin in May, passing poverty, Alan considered how actually alone he'd been since that realization. Few friends – no one to touch him – so he'd turned to stories.

The nation had been turbulent around him, the newspapers flurrying with headlines. Alan's adolescence took place among this agitation. De Valera promised Utopia for small farmers. The first papal emissary arrived, a toad-like man wearing a toad-like hat, who proudly held out his small pudgy hand for mustard smelling kisses. Mussolini entered Abyssinia. The civil war kicked off in Spain. Bishops blessed the ex-hurling players from Ireland who went to fight for Franco. The I.R.A. were still around. One man on a bicycle near Athlone was blown up by his own bomb hidden in a box for Kellogg's

102

cornflakes. Alan read the Russians. Girls noticed his face, dark, different, shadowed. There was talk of war. Alan was seized now by a sexual fantasy rather than a fantasy of history. By the Shannon he imagined a male lover. This love affair was happening in Berlin. Why a male lover? Perhaps the explanation was simple. He had four brothers but no sense of friendship with them. He wanted to be close to another male, make up for the dearth in his own family relationships. In the Berlin of his mind he wore a black, white-spotted tie. A youth bent over him and kissed him. Alan in Dublin passed a lavatory. He entered. He entered really to study the graffiti. It was a time of homosexual craving in Dublin. 'I am a priest. I like little boys.' Alan looking at the lavatory walls saw the wall of his youth, a prison wall now scratched with indecipherable messages. There'd been no one, absolutely no one there. So he'd continued to express himself in words of fiction.

He went to a dance one night, danced with a girl from Dublin, afterwards walked by the Shannon with her. She was of a posh family. She remarked that they had a tennis court at the back of their home in Dublin. That finished Alan's interest in her.

His body had been in turmoil; he'd a pure, white body, in nakedness an angelic, lanky body. In a mirror in his mind Alan saw that body. The glass door of a Dublin pub was ornate beside him. He saw himself, a youth, touching himself, felt the negation. It was a time his body had been most alive, most tender. So instead of touching another person he translated the moments of self-negation into fiction. It had been a strange fiction. It had been about relationships in a world remembered from childhood, a world of history.

History was happening all around him. British diplomats were running back and forth to Germany with increasing agitation. Alan studied for his final examinations. He wrote an essay about Red Hugh O'Donnell.

Passing the red brick buildings of Summerhill, Alan considered Red Hugh O'Donnell as he'd written about him for his final examinations at school, the red-haired youth who'd died at twenty-nine, poisoned by the traitor James Blake in Simancas, laid out far from home. Harvest time that year Alan had left for Dublin; taken the train. There'd been marigolds. He'd worn his long coat. He had said goodbye to Athlone and gone to Dublin to study, among other things, history. Dublin at first had been a room, but the room branched out and became the world. Alan strode today, a new confidence in him. From the rugby changing-rooms of Athlone, from the history lessons about Red Hugh O'Donnell, from the gleaming harvest fields about

Athlone he'd built a statement. Verging on O'Connell Street he was sure of it. He'd write a novel called *A Cavalier against Time* and then leave the shores of this land for ever. Already he was saying goodbye to the rugby changing-rooms of Athlone, to the lavatory graffiti of Fairview, to the Bull Wall. Just then he met a school comrade and spoke of examinations.

I am Alan Mulvanney. Aged twenty-one. Black-haired. Good looking. Alan saw himself in New York beset by young women.

O'Connell Street told the news of the war in newspaper vendors' sheets. The news today was grave but still people chatted and passed items of information merrily. Outside Clearys' a young man sold the *Messenger*.

Alan remembered a phrase he'd written in his school essay about Red Hugh O'Donnell. 'He died young because Ireland cannot accept age.' Alan realized as he approached O'Connell Bridge how many sources had contributed to what he was today; history, people, sounds, landscape. He was born out of the dead body of Red Hugh O'Donnell as much as out of the harvest fields around Athlone. He carried the intricacies of influence with him. He stumbled with sentences and found the first one for his novel. 'Intreat me not to leave thee, or to return from following after thee: for whither thou goest, I will go; and where thou lodgest, I will lodge: thy people shall be my people, and thy God my God.' He would preface his novel with a quotation from Ruth. He envisaged Lorcan reaching for Eleanor, two people from different backgrounds. One day Alan would marry a Russian, a Greek or maybe simply a woman from across the Shannon.

He wanted to go back, find himself at eighteen and bring that self to this sunny day. The Liffey on one hand stretched to the open sea supervised by gruelling looking gulls, on the other hand bore towards the west of Ireland. Along Aston Quay, along Wellington Quay, brushing by huddled Jewish shops in a grand manner, Alan saw Jewish and Irish history merging, both an Irish face and a Jewish face on Ruth. There was the same music for both races, the memory of the same kind of music. Hitler would not be able to eliminate the echo and the insistence of that music. The sun shone on the rings in a Jewish window and Neptunes opened their fish-like mouths on bridges on the Liffey. Alan swayed with the sunshine.

By Christ Church the novel came more quickly. Seventeenth-century Dublin, priests, horses, bishops, drunkards, ale merchants, soldiers, Catholic clerics in blue hose, English merchants, bowlers, wrestlers, fighting cocks, bulls being baited, stuntmen, ruminative lord deputies, yellows, golds, greens, brocade reds. A red flag went

104

up, the red flag of the Ranters, Diggers, Levellers, call them what you like. The red flag, the red flag of inspiration. In an inn off Smock Alley a young English actor whispered to Lorcan about the new movements in England; the movements of freedom. 'Get up and live in the grace of God,' he conspired. Priests ran over urine, wine and pigs' entrails. Alan faced in the direction of Rathmines.

To start creating this novel is to go back a long time; childhood, vases in Roscommon, green leaves on their mildewed white, hints of vermilion. Alan perceived himself, the portrait of a child.

With some pennies in his pocket he sipped a coffee in 'The Milky Way' at Kelly's Corner, a constellation of stars on the sign above the doorway. A dirty proprietor wiped up coffee dribbles and a lady evangelist muttered to herself about salvation.

The road to Rathmines was a lonely one; a different part of Dublin. Here Protestants lived. Alan stalked up Lower Rathmines Road to Rathgar Road. He then turned and saw Dublin. The sea was whisked in mist. He headed down again. The trees were green and leafy and Protestant ladies peered out at him. He wanted to discard his coat but he held on to it. The act of creation, the longed for release, was happening. A child ran across the harvest fields in Roscommon, assimilating himself into history.

As an adolescent he'd wondered why, why the loneliness, the difference. Today it all made sense to him. He was back again in that golden city of childhood, Galway, and its rumours and agitations. Alan, a child, slept, his dreams secure and peaceful. Alan, an adolescent, wrote by lamplight in Athlone. Someone was responding to him. The world was by indirection responding. All these moments, childhood, adolescence, led to this day in Dublin when he saw his own future, a novel, a statement, a work of art.

'I am Alan Mulvanney. Seventeen, someone without hope.' To hide from everyone no longer made sense. Brothers faded and parents. It was just himself today, himself and the world and the swiftness and lightness of his gait.

The sycamores were in blossom on lower Rathmines Road, the elms. Trams rushed past. Tonight Alan would go and speak to the literary elders of Dublin and say, look I have arrived among your company. I have a bucket of wine from Athlone. I am slightly drunk and in love – in love with life, history. Maybe they would not accept his ticket but no harm; it would not be the first time.

In Dublin that day little boys paddled in Dollymount. German spies peeped over their spectacles at newspaper headlines in Bewley's, Westmoreland Street. Genteel ladies gathered around garden hedges.

Prostitutes made love early in the afternoon. Young Irishmen intent on soldiery carried bags through Dublin to the Dun Laoghaire train. Priests, wavering a little, consumed altar wine and Mr. de Valera read poems written by the Irish going west before Cromwell's men, in order to justify his stance of neutrality in the war. A stained glass window sparkled in Bewley's, Grafton Street. A little girl in blue waded with a butterfly net in Saint Stephen's Green which Alan was just about entering.

On a bench in the Green Alan had a conversation with a Protestant lady. She was acquainted with areas around the Shannon. She lived now in Rathgar. She'd been to India. 'War is a terrible thing,' she stated, 'War is unnecessary. War is created by our pre-fixed attitudes. We blame Mr. Hitler now, but don't look into ourselves, our own attitudes. Life ought to be a battle for love, but instead it's a conspiracy of silence about love. This war is created from militarism, misunderstanding between nations. We must now pray and be silent for peace.' Ducks passed on the pond, stopped, looked interested. Alan went on.

Grafton Street became Leningrad, Dublin became the queen of cities. Alan faced down the street. He'd never forget this day. Trains ran to the Russian countryside, but in the city wise men paused over coffee. Dublin and Leningrad joined hands and for one moment in his life Alan felt himself riding on the universal. Grafton Street became the world, became hope, became youth. Ladies in black stooped out of Johnson Court church.

A moment in the history of Alan's mind became a moment in my own history. I picked up the sense of that afternoon on Grafton Street. I turned towards Eugene and Cherine and felt happy to be alive.

The nights still bore their own degree of unrest. In strawberry underpants turning, I felt charged by waves of desire, of sexual tremors. The main street, the girls had always been a sexual release. Now I philosophised about poetry. But always in bed I was restrained. Compassion had entered my life, care.

'Intreat me not to leave thee, or to return from following after thee: for whither though goest, I will go; and where thou lodgest, I will lodge: thy people shall be my people, and thy God my God.'

Alan was in one of those white shirts his mother had ironed. The Shannon was brimming that evening. Rouge in it, gold flecks. Eileen was in her blue dress. It was on a slope by the Shannon they met. All the months of wandering, of indecision led to this encounter for Alan. The last excited sunsets in Dublin before he'd left it. Women near Amiens Street station at night. Men cloaked by the war. 'Jaysus I'm

106

horny tonight.' Dublin, a mantle, evening in May, became an evening when lipstick rained on the Shannon. Eileen's brothers had been farting and emitting the odours of their arms around the house all that day. She'd escaped. Alan's curls on his forehead were relics. That evening Alan's mother had bid him be wary of opportunist women. Eileen had taken a slip of paper with her in the car to read about a Hollywood film star discussing soap. They were from opposite sides of the Shannon. They moved towards one another in the harvest fields. His mother's giant iron pounded in Alan's head. The geese screamed in Eileen's. They moved towards one another to talk. Alan saw his mother's iron reflecting the sunset of Athlone. Eileen recalled the words of wisdom of a young woman who'd accompanied her on this trip. 'Never let a good looking young man out of your fingers.' Someone sneezed. The tableau was arrested. Before touching, before reaching towards one another Alan and Eileen became an image, the sounds in the background dying into an echo, and the image transfixed – like history, like a stained glass window in a small church. Mentally I prayed that they could properly reach to one another, but before any such liaison could take place the picture froze. I was caught with a memory that would always have stopped in motion.

Eugene lay back on the grass. I kissed his chest. Cherine spluttered with laughter and told me I was being fashionable. Sitting on her hunkers she then looked domineeringly towards a civil war ruin. I prayed to God that my small bit of happiness would last; that Alan and Eileen could be moved to wander again, that their paths could unfold into a mutual one and an old enigma, an old question of personal history could be resolved. Just then my father was fired from his job and with a suitcase left for England to seek work and a new home for his wife and son.

Now that they were thinking of going back to England, my mother was struck by the fact that in all these years she had not inquired after Alan or discovered any information about his present whereabouts – and it had been he in a way who'd brought her back to Ireland.

So one morning, 17 May, she serenely set out. It was a fine day. On the station platform two women stood beside one another, herself and Mrs Houlihan, leader of the urban council and only now catching her breath after the 1916 celebrations. Otherwise there were few people on the platform. Both women stood near a poster advertising the Côte d'Azur. Both were in black. Mrs. Houlihan's eyes were on Mrs. Hitchens. At last the zebra had got out of the zoo and stood beside her on a station platform.

Mrs. Houlihan had been the third child of a well-to-do Dublin family. Their house had been on Sandford Road, a generously proportioned, red brick house sidling inquisitively towards the road. Mrs. Houlihan had grown up listening to the legends of Ireland – in Gaelic. Her father, a civil servant, made sure she knew about Cúchulainn and Ruairc Mac Suibhne. In her white blouse she crouched on the carpet, forever tentative and wakeful towards these stories. They were the treasures of Ireland. At a very young age she was dispatched off to the Blasket Islands – to perfect her Gaelic. She was riding into the Land of Youth. Nuns in Stephen's Green would have no hold on her now. A girl in a black school coat stood in the bow of the boat. Hares gallivanted in the Blaskets. Marigolds saturated the poor land in the August sunsets. In her blue and white summer dress, in her black shining shoes, strapped on her cream skin, she ran. She ran until she ran into the arms of a young man. Cúchulainn, Ruairc Mac Suibhne became a local lad. At seventeen she made love among the marigolds, voyeuristic hares creeping up on them. It was this occurrence she was thinking about this morning as she observed Mrs. Hitchens, as one would an opera singer taken to prostitution or a circus star gone varicose. Mrs. Houlihan thought of chests of nipples, of genitals and the Gaelic words for these things 'Cliabh, sine . . ' She thought of them because her existence subsequently had been so devoid of these things; marriage, a personal exodus west, life with a coal merchant husband in a small town – and he cringing and gnarled with age as if carrying all the coal bags had done it – a stupid son. Mrs. Houlihan looking at Mrs. Hitchens knew she'd been betrayed. A casket of marigolds had been taken from her. Somewhere along the way she'd been duped and had duped herself. She was old, barren, overweight now. Her eyes narrowed as a hen's glistening blue eyes, in front of the poster celebrating the Côte d'Azur. 'Lachai, tell us that story again . . .' Lachai had since gone to New York or San Francisco. Lachai was dead.

The train pulled over the bridge. Eileen sat near Mrs. Houlihan. There was a delicate thread of recognition, of mutual acceptance but of silence between them. Mrs. Houlihan's hair-brush brows bristled over spectacles as she disapproved of the headlines in the *Irish Independent*. Her scarf kept her head from burgeoning with distress. Eileen considered where Mrs. Houlihan would be going to – Dublin – and she wondered if she herself should bypass Athlone and go on to Dublin. What would Dublin be like this fine day?

Dublin would be different but it would still be a city of young men. There'd still be young men in gleaming white shirts streaming out of

Trinity; today there would be green everywhere and churches would stand proudly . . . Saint Audoen's, Saint Michan's. What then would mark a city in 1966 off from a city in 1943? The usual quota of mods and rockers would be standing around, licking an ice-cream maybe in the middle of the road in Merrion Street where it dove like a chasm to the Peppercannister. A sprightly girl in a mini skirt would be waving her perfumes down Grafton Street. The sea of bicycles would be diminished slightly. But there was more than that. Those young students coming out of Trinity College would have different questions on their faces. The Book of Kells, open inside Trinity, would augur a different chapter for them. 'We were more innocent then,' she told herself as if she had been a member of the Trinity cricket team in 1943, 'There was more innocence in our acts.'

She saw a young Trinity student, his head riven by a song he'd heard the previous night, rise early one morning in May 1943 in his room over 'The Milky Way' at Kelly's Corner, stumble to the window in his underpants and salute an elm outside. Below in the café Alan Mulvanney ruminated over a novel he'd contemplated in this place two years before which he was now completing. The train groaned to a halt in Athlone; shaking Eileen out of her reverie and the whim of journeying on to Dublin. Clutching her handbag she wandered into the streets of Athlone.

'When Edmund Spenser arrived in Munster he found a country which bewitched him; this country was a paradise pervaded by silent, atavistic eyes. Eyes peered over bushes of fuschia. Edmund Spenser was here long enough to see this country torn aounder, the fuschia, the eyes destroyed; Ireland became a nightmare, a low moan on the roads, bodies of those that survived withered and gnarled to maggots, and the land of Munster, the domain of the Fitzgeralds and the Desmonds blackened and the last choking of a pheasant silenced.'

Visiting Athlone was like visiting a town in which a world-famous writer had been born. Eileen stood over the knitwear in the shop windows reverentially looking at it. Athlone had changed; its shopfronts had become crass and ugly. But Eileen felt only the wine under her feet and smelt the lichen from gaps in the walls of dark alleyways. By the Shannon a little boy confronted her. He was in a blue and white striped T-shirt, his hands behind his back. His hair was marmalade colour and so were his freckles. He smiled. The smile, slow at first, broadened to near mirth, the little boy recognising a kindred spirit in Eileen. She smiled back. Boats swayed on the Shannon. 'What did you find out at school today?' Questions poured through Eileen's mind without being asked out loud. But the little boy picked up the sense of her questions and telepathic answers returned. 'I learnt about Red Hugh O'Donnell and Eoin Ruadh O'Súilleabháin.' Reams of blue striped white jotting paper streamed from the little boy's eyes. His eyes were blobs of pale blue school ink. A battalion of buttercups sprang by his loosely laced boots. This silent conversation might have overwhelmed them both had not Eileen been tugged by the demands of other venues and sights in Athlone.

'He who knows nothing, loves nothing. He who can do nothing understands nothing. He who understands nothing is worthless. But he who understands also loves, notices, sees . . . The more knowledge is inherent in a thing the greater the love . . . Anyone who imagines all fruits ripen at the same time as the strawberries knows nothing about grapes.' Retracing her steps up an alleyway Eileen was daunted by the realization that Alan might be the teacher of the little boy. How were the grapes fermenting? Did the vines still crawl around the convent of San Pietro in Montorio, Rome where O'Neill and O'Donnell were buried. Did the noses of their Celtic corpses still rub in the green grapes they'd never seen at home? When I was little in Newcastle a woman from Athlone called and informed my mother of Alan's abortive trip to Rome. That trip had magnified in her mind. Today in Athlone imaginatively she reached a city more full of youth than Dublin. She was following a lad in an orange T-shirt through the squares. His arms were frail as bird's wings. In a café he danced with her. A tango. The post-war band started up. The lights became blue. Girls in navy dresses soured, their arms folded. Old men shivered over walking sticks. 'Yes?' A waitress gruffly asked Eileen what she wanted. 'Coffee.' Eileen slipped away to the toilet where she produced a stick of slimy, London, carmine lipstick. Her face in the mirror had become very old. 'Slaimhníonn se uainn fé mar a slaimhníonn an t-uisce de gaineamh an trá' – 'It slips from us as the water slips from the sand of the shore.' On the train home that evening Eileen's head reclined in sleep. She heard music again, not the music of a tango flaring up, but an Irish battle lament. Alan's portrait had survived, intact.

Cherine made up little stories which accommodated both herself and Eugene. He was an aristocratic member of the Wild Geese. She was the poor peasant girl who mourned his flight from Ireland. Cherine had one fantasy above all others. She was married to Eugene McDermott, living with him in a house on the main street, knitting his jerseys of many colours and patterns which chimed with his rolling auburn hair, teaching their child Gaelic and bringing him to see *Bambi*, as her mother had brought her, in the local decrepit cinema.

This fantasy might have been closer to the balance of her ancestry than were the forlorn postures of the stories she made up. Her family had hit the roads by being drop-outs from the exodus west according to her father, burghers from Drogheda and Dundalk overloaded with silver and gold. Cherine wanted to re-enter a house in Drogheda or Dundalk now, recapture the silver and gold. A house full of big rooms of dark floorboards in this town would suffice. A child cried on these floorboards, beckoning Cherine to her destiny. To move this destiny one stage forward Cherine privately made an arrangement with Eugene to visit the ruin of a medieval convent outside town. She suggested this expedition as if her interest in history would curdle her with its intensity. Eugene looked at her blankly, wandering why I wasn't to be included, but like so many of her plans before he accepted it at face value. They moved off from the prom before I could arrive. Cherine, decked out in a strawberry cardigan, one of her lineage from childhood, lustfully eyed the stripes on Eugene's T-shirt. It was a glorious day, the white hawthorn blazing along the way, clouds basking on high. 'Cromwell's men made the nuns take their gowns over their heads and do a naked jig in the clover,' was her father's version of events surrounding the convent. Naked nuns lined the roadside now, waving their gowns above their heads, wishing Cherine luck in her mission. Eugene, drawing near her, insisted on dissertations on Russian literature, but Cherine ruefully diverted the topic, dwelling on all the lewd incidents she could gather from Russian literature. Somehow Eugene tuned into the tone of her wishes and lapsed into silence. She had him help her over the ditch when the ruin came in sight and she tried to hold on to that hand. But that hand pulled away and again she followed Eugene. Behind the ruin, gold scintillating furze at her feet, in full view of a granny sheep, an outbuilding of the mental hospital distantly rearing an eye, Cherine proceeded to remove her cardigan, let slip the top of her white, black-speckled dress and was about to shed her bra when Eugene stated, straight and unabashed, 'It's not necessary.' A child cried on dark floorboards in a long room in a big house. But he cried in vain. Cherine could not reach him now. Eugene had killed the child they would have together.

> So ferry 'cross the Mersey
> Cos this land's the place I know
> And here I'll stay.

My father returned from England. He had a job – as a foreman in a factory in London – and a council flat in White City. We were to leave on 23 June. Savagely I bashed at my guitar. I'd taken fright at the first inkling of Cherine turning away from me, abandoned the prom, climbed the spiral of nights again, this time on a coterie of songs. This time I danced in the local ballroom, loosely fingering the backsides of nearly toothless, middle-aged women, baby-faced showband singers almost eating the microphones like cabbages.

It was the time of processions in town. Creamy girls frothed the street with pink petals shaken from baskets. Little boys in their first holy communion suits, claret dickie bows lecherously ajar, straddled the square. Priests, cloaked in gold, generously clouded the air with incense. The Sacred Heart was posited outside sweetshops beside bowls of pink roses and, in one shop window the portrait of a young man in American military uniform stood alongside packets of Kellogg's cornflakes and a bowl of pink roses. This young man had originally lived in the town, made a local girl pregnant, left in disgrace and subsequently triumphed in the American air force. To make good his name his mother faithfully placed his picture in the shop window instead of that of the Sacred Heart each June.

There'd been ragged, undulating processions along by the Shannon when Mrs. McDermott was young, veils of little girls visions against the sun, the crucifix borne aloft, looking none the better for being exposed to the light after months in dust laden enclosure. Processions had become rides in Ford Tudor Vauxhalls to dances, a cortège of cars streaming to dances by the Shannon still pink with midsummer light and bearing up swans, lilies and enmeshed reeds. The rides to dances became in turn the face of a young man. It was not of this young man, of Spain, or red scarves Mrs. McDermott was thinking when she confronted her son Eugene. Her basket was crammed with vegetables alongside her short sleeved, floral summer dress. She'd heard. Her son was having an affair with the tinker girl. Eugene was forbidden to see her again. Anyway it was too late. The space by the prom was just a monument now; little old ladies in black stopped in vain for snatches of Russian poetry. Disappointed they wobbled home, sprinkled paprika on their unsuspecting Siamese cats.

'Jeremy.' I was taking a stroll by the prom one evening. I'd changed from wearing the black leather slightly shorn jacket I'd sported to the dances to clothing myself in bright blue denim. There was still pink in the sky, colonies and zones of insects inhabiting the outskirts of trees. Soon we would be leaving. Light was all but fading on photographs of young working-class local lads who'd gone to fight for the king in the First World War – lulled by the rhetoric of middle-class Irish politicians – and were blown apart. I immersed myself in the fate of their doleful eyes, in the brave front of their military lapels. Since my parents had been forced to rediscover their working-class roots I made tentative moves towards a new identity; I rolled out the red carpet. This evening I was carrying dead comrades on Flanders Fields, being blasted among the poppies, when Cherine stepped out from behind a maple trunk and surprised me. She did not have to ask. She wished to be brought to the dance.

She was wearing her party dress, a blue taffeta one in which her mother had won a ballroom dancing competition in Carlisle. Tightly she clung to my thighs. The red light spun round us, the wave of a wand. The girl singer mourned Arkansas. Cherine tugged my hand with her effervescent, pale, tiny one and led me into the night.

She repeated fragments of this town's history to me, like a mantra, as she pulled me along by the canal. The view of the town was good. The monks, the vagrant saints – mesmerised with their own holiness – the chiefs, the kings, the ponies of kings, the wives, the adulterers, the poor, the poets, the latter day peasants. All were called upon. Cherine had me kneel as the chill of a holy well slapped our faces. Insects talked at the stems of long grasses. There was a little suffusion of pink still in the sky; was it twilight or dawn? Cherine leaned back and confronted the sky.

A fat, middle-aged, beer-smelling stranger followed a woman up a narrow and creaking stairs in Los Angeles. His shirt was patterned with goods from the American arms industry. In a tiny room on a bed she opened her legs for him. A little poodle, smelling of the latest doggie perfume, yelped, recalling sorties on bogs in Ireland under talcum clouds once.

Cherine was sure of it now. Her illustrious cousin had fallen to infamy. 'In 1660 the crowds gathered on the main street on the restoration of the king, singing "Thugamar Fein an Samradh Linn" – "We Bring the Summer with Us."' Cherine unbuckled my gold belt with my initial on it, which survived from England. I didn't want to make love to her. I watched her do it. I looked at the cleanness of my denim trousers and then she became like all of the little factory girls, gasping . . .

'Eugene.' Eugene was walking by the prom in his fawn jacket. It was evening. Pink still in the sky. Midsummer nearly garrulous in the trees. Suddenly Cherine appeared like an apparition from behind an undergrown oak. 'Eugene, I'm sorry.' With that she disappeared, defying the imagination as to how swiftly she flitted away.

Eugene continued on his way. His shoulders seemed more hunched

113

than before. Approaching the road he was in time to see some young foreigners cycling by, pastel lemons, maroons, greens. Foreign voices muffled into one another. Then they were gone. When Eugene arrived home he didn't have to open the door. His parents did it for him. His father, out for a walk himself, had spied over a wall Eugene stop with the tinker girl. Mr. McDermott's hand landed on him with uncustomary violence. Eugene was kicked up the stairs. In his efforts to show how good a parent he could be for once, his father smashed the glass on a photograph of the rugby boys of 1933 in blue and white striped jerseys – he was there with extremely illuminated red hair – and that made him madder. Eugene's mother was heard to spit, 'The likes of that one. The likes of that one.' Eugene was pushed into his room. Before she slammed the door Mrs. McDermott hit him with such ferocity he cried out. The tears were streaming from his eyes a long time after she was gone and when he turned to the window, as if the thought had not occurred to him before to look out of this prison. There were swifts outside, glad and jittery, in the pink air over the pink river, but Eugene saw a woman sitting quietly, sitting contentedly in a café in Bucharest, under a bunch of autumn marigolds, her unhurried hand on a glass of white wine.

'Take that, you git.' Some evenings before leaving Ireland my mother broke every single one of her John McCormack records, speaking to them first. 'That's what you deserve,' she told 'The Croppy Boy'. 'There you go,' she sneered with malice at 'I'll take you home again Kathleen' before hurling it. 'Now see what you've come to,' she reviled 'Panus Angelicus' but, for some reason, when it came to the turn of 'The Kerry Dance' she cried before breaking it.

A man in a pub in this town had told her during her sojourn here how Count John McCormack once returned to sing in his native Athlone and only five people turned up.

I left Ireland on 23 June 1966. Dates had been rearranged and my parents left on separate days from that originally planned. The previous night I'd toured the town, gone to Cherine's home, the door slyly opened and Martin Finnerty telling me his daughter was not in, I went to Eugene's home. That little home proved deaf. On the main street I said goodbye to Ireland.

I left Ireland with my guitar, a rucksack and a poem by Eugene McDermott I still treasure. It was entitled 'A Curious Street.'

Lights twinkle, it's that horizon once more.
Trains shunt and start, you know you've
Won. A curious street unfolds –

Pictures. Pictures of girls foot-falling
With library books and hair-pin dreams.
We've won, we've won you tell her shadow –
But now the engines grunt. The train
Tears towards Leningrad, Moscow, New York.
I've lost you, have I? Am I alone in a corridor of chairs?

Lights twinkle. Trains dash and appease. You've lost so much.
But they couldn't tear your heart out in rags however they tried.
I sit and try, try to remember the day
I first loved you and you cried 'We won't
Be together when you build a house!'
The house stands now. I interpret it in books and shadows –
And I move on. There are other fingers to touch.

Standing on the platform, waiting for the train, in a white, open-necked shirt, my guitar planked alongside me, marigolds brimming in the background, Alan's question came to me again, one asked at a crib in Athlone Christmas 1943, one repeated by me beside a crib in this town with my mother alongside me. Why the duality? Why negation alongside tenderness? Why the pink illumined Christ child in a world where cities are being razed and little Jewish children walking into gas chambers eating chocolate? In the heat of the afternoon, the grief, the experience of loss inside me almost too much to bear, my pain washed into the pallor of the air, the torpor of the marigolds, the brightness of the limestone, the white collar of my shirt which my mother had graciously ironed before leaving, the corridors of remembrance, of identification thrown open in me, I was forced to renegue my own pain and become, imagine, the pain of others. In this way, I found an answer to Alan's question, however inadequate.

I was leaving one place for another and I became other people who'd left their homes, either for a day or a lifetime. I experienced their pain, the distinctiveness of their dress and the memory of their eyes. It wasn't just that I assuaged my own pain but something was momentarily created: meaning, music, the intensity of marigolds. I saw the question in Alan's eyes again and I realized I'd inadvertently come up with an answer; to become one with another, despite the battering of cities or the falling of bombs, is to establish a memory of hope and a home for the Christ child Alan so fondly confronted at the crib in Athlone when his mother was fretting about her Christmas cake – was it all right? – and trying to drag him into a night when the frost rose in wisps from the Shannon.

It is spring 1947. A woman waits for the train. She's just come from the bed of a farmer, having robbed him of his money so she has to get out of the country quickly. The lewd things he made her do last night. The bastard. But she's got him now. He's sleeping like a pig at this moment, grunting like a cow in labour, his pink fat bottom above the bed clothes. She got hold of his money. Under the floorboards. So as dawn came she cycled away, grabbed her case and made off. Hollywood here I come. This morning by the station she looks quiet, reflective even. Black hair rolls on the orangeade shoulders of her coat. In 1947 her clothes are already old-fashioned. She stands very erect. As she waits her fretting goes and she thinks of the number of memories her eyes will bring to the silver screen in Hollywood. They will bring her tinker memories. The valleys of Munster, lush and gold. The main street of a town on which the bodies of tinkers were wheeled up, corpse piled upon corpse, on barrows to the workhouse during the Famine. Genocide, the wilfulness of England towards Ireland, the wilfulness of the present middle-class population towards the tinker people. Some of her relatives are still on the roads. A young man sells jettisoned clocks from his van. Some older relatives still tour in palatial caravans of emerald, lemon and red. Only last week she heard of a lost uncle who keeps a herd of black spotted, white ponies by Lettergesh Beach in Connemara. Her eyes will bring the memory of small town sex. The initial pilgrimage of young boys towards her body. Later the fumbling hands of older men. But the nicest time was with a deaf and dumb youth. By the canal. It was she who did the seducing. She was in a white dress with a lace cover of white with pink spots and this outfit allowed the sun to play through. She cavorted about, knowing the ethereal effect she must have been having, and then bid the boy kneel and took his inarticulate penis and spoke to it. She lay back as he came in her and in view of the distant church she repeated to herself the most cogent history lessons she'd learnt at school. 'Wolfe Tone cut his throat. Parnell committed adultery with Kitty O'Shea.' For one moment history became real. She cried out. 'Jesus, Mary and Joseph.' The deaf and dumb youth crawled away like a stealthy animal. She lay, a heap of garments, crying for all things which could neither hear nor speak. More than anything her eyes will bring the memory of waiting to the silver screen, waiting in cafés. Oh yes, she's been to 'The Milky Way' in Dublin. All her life she's waited: as a child for the films to arrive in tin cans like milk containers outside the local cinema; as an adult for coffees. She's often prayed as she waited, and now by the station her tableaux of sex turn to prayer. 'Mary and Jesus bring me safe to Hollywood.'

116

It is a morning in June 1939. A woman stands on a station platform in County Meath. She's going to take a train to Dublin where she will buy yet another brown suit, this time for her sister's wedding in September. Purple lilac dashes against red, rusted railings. The woman is back again, married, in the county of her childhood. Already her husband is talking vivaciously about the coming Galway races. A pony and trap left her at the station this morning. The kitchen as she left it reeked of home-made butter and garlands of hollyhocks and asters which have sneaked in from the garden. The garden is behind the big house, looking to expanses of scintillating fields in which poised thoroughbreds canter. Today she will not just try on a brown suit but also revel a little, have a sherry, gaze at the gulls on the Liffey from O'Connell Bridge, feed the ducks in Stephen's Green, speculate on the forthcoming wedding; what are people to wear? A cloud goes over and momentarily darkens the station. Sometimes, as she makes brown bread in her cerise blouse, as she intrudes into the garden, checking a contrary, unopened plant, she remembers. I was a child here. White clouds still puff in wide spaces over the fields but a shadow creeps over her. She has returned to the county of her childhood. She has come back for some reason. All her life she sought a first image behind the shadows of childhood, but the further she went the more surrounded she was by shadows. In the place of thickest shadow – Germany – she was nearest to placing her hands behind the mirror and touching – a woman in an Edwardian white dress, her mother, herself as a child untrammelled by shadows. Now after all the years she has come home and, despite sunshine, still hears the march of military footsteps and sees the turrets over Protestant cemeteries. What had she known before all these contagions of fears, sounds, hushes? This morning, standing by the station she sees what she's been looking for. She sees her own coming death. In a brown suit, hair in a bun, lace at her neck, she looks not unlike how she will look on an imminent Mass card. The phantom lingers just as long as the train doesn't come. Her eyes like Nostradamus' conjure a future world – miles of mountainside, suburban houses – but there'll be no children of her own in this world. She'll never have children. Why then this pressing feeling of posterity, of continuity; why the little boy in a blue and white striped jersey running by a beach?

It is June 1946. A young man leaves home. He is standing awkwardly and forlornly on the station platform. For a long time he's been thinking of going, years. Only now does he do it. He is in a white, open-necked shirt. He looks totally self-conscious as if someone is looking at him, picturing him. He's from the countryside near this town; his parents have a farm. He has one brother, little – red-haired, like himself. Sometimes he pushes this little boy on a swing at the end of the garden beside the farmhouse. When he was small he was full of fear. Fear of a room at the top of the house, empty and long, which was haunted. Fear of school. The teacher dwelt on the macabre incidents of history in the tiny, marooned schoolhouse. Fear of the countryside about their home. Old farmers frequently hung themselves in it and shadows brushed over all the time, long trailing shadows, over the piquantly green, virgin forests which had sprung up only since the coming into being of the new state. By the station the young man talks to himself. He addresses himself as Michael. He talks about childhood, about his family, particularly his parents who hated his going. Why is he leaving? Always there has been a shadow that has pursued him and now he wants to get away from that shadow. He felt it most forcibly in the room at the top of the house. Fear. Awkwardness. Simply lack of poise. Once at a marquee dance he met a girl who invited him into the coloured lights outside. The band played 'My Bonnie lies over the Ocean'. She told him he had lovely eyes and that he'd go far. She had black hair. She was in a blue dress. As it was late summer there was a spattering of freckles on her face. Eileen Carmody she said her name was. He asked her if she was a gypsy and she said no, she was a whore. That must have been six years ago. Yesterday he took a little trip into the lime corn, sauntering in it. In the same white shirt he wears today. And as he walked, diminishing prospective poppies under his feet, it seemed for the first time he was going through the shadow, cutting through the malevolent lion-like clocks of the farmhouse, the country roads which eddied with cycling bachelors, the trees on which people hung themselves. He was flying through the yellow ochre wallpaper. He was going to the other side of the shadow. He would not be here to see the corn ripen this year but, for one moment, he had transcended the maledictions. He was in orbit. In this orbit he saw past, present and future. He saw the sums on the blackboard in the school-room, he saw the twin books which lay about the house – a black-leather-covered Bible, a farmers' almanac – he saw the ghost of the empty room at the top of the house where he was frequently locked as punishment, a lady with a banana black face, and his amazement, as he cowered in the corner, when she ventured onto the red carpet at the top of the stairs outside. He remembered a girl who'd been locked in a chicken hut on a neighbouring farm for years because of some mental aberration in her and the fuss there was when she was found; she

118

became a kind of folk heroine, the *Irish Independent* clicking a camera at her in the farmyard. He'd envied her success and wished to achieve something like it. Already in the corn he felt the cringing farewell his parents would give him, the two of them standing by the kitchen table, looking away from him, as he'd be leaving, his little brother helplessly looking up at him, the clocks clanking, the sheepdog whinging, fishes' heads stored in newspaper for the cats. Already the bombed-out avenues of Notting Hill stretched, the unwelcoming notices waiting – 'No Blacks or Irish need apply' – conspiratorial smoke curling in Irish pubs, middle-aged men smoking pipes over the cards they were handling. But more than anything he felt the moment he was in, the sky above, the corn, the poppies by his feet. In the intensity bought by the act of leaving he became a child again with the perceptions of a child. Years peeled away. He was veering through a blockade created by experience. The sun whipped overhead, light played on the tops of elms bordering the cornfield, the young man's arms were outstretched. In his white shirt he muttered to the blue of the sky, to the dead in a nearby, hillside cemetery. A shadow built by pain was demolished and the young man's face became very clear, freezing as the deception of time was broken within him and his features converged on the features of another young man in another time. As I waited for the train I was amazed by the particularity of everything, my white shirt, the fuschia thrust up against the sea of black bog surrounding the station, the donkeys wandering on the road through the bog, the poppies nodding at the sides of the bog and cider of the road. I was amazed in spite of myself, at the wound which was throbbing inside me, at the extent to which I found I'd been affected by the place now that I was leaving. I was amazed at the hurt I felt, by the lack of acceptance of me here, by the gap, the gap in people's minds, the gap in my dual heritage, the gap which always seemed to prevail here between trying to reach and reaching. More than anything I was amazed at the way a bed of marigolds seemed to absorb all that was in my eyes and cleanse me of pain. The train came and I left, thinking I would not be back for a long time.

Cherine found she was pregnant. In the depths of the bath tub in the bathroom beside the cemetery she tried to exterminate the life within her with knitting needles. An ambulance screamed to the cemetery, throwing out its banshee light as it stood stationary near the cemetery gates. Already the women were out in nightdresses. Eugene McDermott had impregnated the tinker girl and she'd tried to murder the life within her. The prospective child within Cherine was saved. Some weeks later, mid-August, Cherine found herself packing in her bedroom beside the cemetery, tearing down the ikons of Montgomery Clift in the process.

Tonight I see them all, Cherine and those I most immediately associate with that time. All but one seems unaffected by the events that involved them. Cherine kneels by the fireplace in the sitting-room of a big house on the main street of a small town. Behind her, her husband reads a newspaper, sunk into a chair. They got married last Christmas. Cherine was in a flowing white. A young solicitor married the owner of a boutique. Everything was going fine until Martin Finnerty decided to collect money door to door for a party for the newly weds, doing a jig, playing a few bars in a ward in the hospital for this purpose. They quickly locked him in the mental hospital where he still is. Cherine's pregnant again. In a short black dress she stares into the fire. Her husband mumbles something to himself and the street outside is silent.

Although it is winter I see Eugene in summer. He is walking along by the Thames with a young black boy. The sun is sinking over the warehouses and the derelict buildings. The little boy tugs Eugene's hand and brings him to a council flat where, over the Thames, a woman moans gently about Annse d'Ennerie and Savannah de la Mar, a young man turning to her in a field of cane.

My mother passes a Catholic church in White City. She pauses and thinks to go in but then remembers and goes on.

It is silent in Belfast. The orange light seems to answer to the orange light of a street in a small town but borders of disconsolate grief separate these milieux, a militia that wander the night, young I.R.A. men in Milltown cemetery, dead spinsters in the cemetery beside Cherine's former home. A saracen pulls in, momentarily disrupting the silence, an alsatian leaping out, whining for the neon of Belfast. Then there's silence again. The Queen and Prince Philip range alongside proud tableaux of women's pubic hair. The Union Jack is safe and sound here. Young men sleep under graffiti. 'Remember Saint Ives June 1976'. The portrait of a young man holding a medallion burns more luminously than ever but this time, by default, by insanity, he is a military man. Young soldiers of another army crouch over blazing open-air army fires in Europe, recalling their heritage, in part his own. Alan Mulvanney has conquered the night.

But winter quiet or not, events of the past still go on regardless of the fact they have passed into history. A fifteen-year-old girl waits on a station platform in County Galway, August 1966, scarf around her head, bewilderment and confusion in her face, on her way to England to have her baby, the marigolds still scorching in the background and her little body looking as if it will suffocate in its grey winter coat. But as she waits another language creeps into the pink of her eyes, a secret language, a language always under the surface of things, rising to a pitch now and drowning out the sound of the incoming train. 'After a while Eleanor tired of the rats and the corpses. She'd take little trips by herself through the winter, fog-bound, death-bound city. Malaria, dysentery, spotted fever; these were the whispers in the air. A dying priest read a book under the Market Cross. Women waited anxiously by the quays. Every day one wondered if Charles, Duke of Lorraine would send a ship. Ships came all right, phantom ships. Ships reeled through Galway as women moaned and swayed in their last hours. Even the cormorants, used to catch herring, were dying. But, as Eleanor O'Keefe pattered through Galway, the image of another city gradually rose from this one. It came together, piece by piece. She saw it in the nearly eyeless sockets of an old lady. She imagined it in the dead hand of a little boy reaching onto the steps from the black quayside water. It was a city which recollected her earliest youth. In her youth boats came from Europe bearing rolls of gold velvet and satin and she and her brother and his foster-brother wrapped themselves in them as if they'd been brought especially for them. A naked boy held gold satin to his body. There'd been secret heirlooms of silver bodkins in the cellars of their castle and amethyst rings old ladies jealously buried in their drawers. Eleanor missed her brother; she missed him and his foster-brother. She saw her brother's body bound by gold satin, his albino nipples, the blond hair falling off his shoulders. Among the smell of death she smelt the odours of his body, restless adolescent ones. He was her angel now and he pointed the way back to childhood, but childhood was another country. It no longer lay in this nation but in another one, and she could go there only alone. Lorcan stirred their paltry remains of oatmeal in infested water. She watched him. The city and the country she was going to was clear now; there were little corridors of laneways in the city, canals, wildly curtsying willow trees, autumn oaks, and bridges over the canals where men extravagantly made way for you. It was a city which succeeded the images of her childhood and a country evolved from the pursuit of the past. The voice of one searching truth was quelled and one was satisfied with silver and gold. It was not she told herself she was reneguing on truth; she had given much of herself to truth. Her brother, his foster-brother had been sacrificed to truth and now she had to replenish the coffers. The winter glades were gone, the nights the two boys slept together in a pair of red pantaloons they'd found in an empty house near Drogheda, the nights Lorcan and herself sat up making up little stories and the bishop farted voluminously in his sleep and whispered sacred prayers simultaneously. Lorcan turned to her and mentioned some thought Augustine of Hippo had vouched about suffering but she just stared past him and saw herself in a gold bodice, a trailing gold petticoat by a window of occasional blue and red diamond shapes, part of a roll of newly arrived gold satin in her hand and she caressing her slender features with it against the light which came in from the foreign city and the foreign country outside.'

[9]

The autumn of 1966 was the most normal time in my life. I met up with Cherine again and we became boyfriend and girlfriend. I wore a red jacket again, not the teddyboy one of five years before, but a broader, more wholesome one, a mod's one. My hair was neatly cut. Two red jackets were a bridge connecting the green of north-eastern England with the sporadic, famished green of London. I worked as an assistant in a greengrocer's in Shepherd's Bush. Cherine minded her sister's expanded number of children in Hackney. I held her hand along Tottenham Court Road. Her hair was newly straightened; despite her pregnancy she'd become slimmer and she transported this slimness in a short black dress, strapped across her naked shoulders – her legs moved like stilts, with the earnest fragility of a young girl's legs. The lights made way for us; they stood back for the majesty of our approach. We had the right faces, wore the right clothes, made the right duality and on this impression were often called in from the night. We were brushed into parties. We were never asked our names, never interrogated about our backgrounds. We just danced until the caves of our minds crashed with lyrics. 'I love the colourful clothes she wears, And the way the sunlight plays upon her hair. I hear the sound of a gentle word On the wind that lifts her perfume through the air.' A jaded TV personality in a lavender shirt, whose hair was a smothering of white over neatly groomed grey, informed Cherine at a party one night that her shoulders were reminiscent of swan's wings. She was more sober in the Continental Café on Charing Cross Road after that. Her head dipped towards her coffee. I touched

122

her chin. She smiled at me from her mascara eyes. I never made love to Cherine. One night in White City, when my parents were away up north, I slept beside her. Lights peered in from other council flats through the window on which the curtains were not drawn. My hand groped for the rising mound of her stomach, my child. 'She left her neighbourhood in which Everyone was filthy rich. She left her parents' home and strayed With a vagabond who made Vows of love she'd never heard, And she believed his every word. She left no forwarding address, Just took her youth and happiness, As with the boy she vanished in The secret sweetness of their sin.' My mother had become a kind of methodist, reforming her appearance, putting the first words of 'The Lord is my Shepherd' – embroidered in gold and green, embodied in a frame – on the wall. My father had adapted serenely to his new modest position. We were a happy family at last. But sometimes my mother crept like a spy, tightly clothed in scarf and coat, to an Irish club where she seated herself on one of the back benches among the emerald walls, studying the graffiti, listening to the little boys in first holy communion suits sing, watching a plaintive game of darts. It rained a lot on Cherine and me. I left her at bus-stops frequently, and watched the buses travel away with her. My way home was usually on a tube which I entered, dazed-eyed. 'I thought love was only true in fairy tales And for someone else but not for me. Love was out to get me, that's the way it seemed, Disappointment haunted all my dreams. Then I saw her face, Now I'm a believer not a trace of doubt in my mind, I'm in love, I'm a believer, Couldn't leave her if I tried.' By accident Cherine and I walked into an Irish pub. We would have made to go – Cherine's hair was enfondled in a funereal black chiffon scarf – but we were compelled to silence by the girl singer sitting on the raised level, her long black hair radically falling and her vowels soaring, loudly and remonstratingly, into the microphone.

You have taken the East from me;
You have taken the West from me;
You have taken what is before me and what is behind me;
You have taken the moon, you have taken the sun from me,
And my fear is great that you have taken God from me!

The odd thing was that Eugene, when all the fuss had died down a little, crept back to the prom. The scarlet bench was newly painted and it scintillated. Curled golden leaves approached him like balls. Little old ladies in black – the non-gossipy ones – returned to admire his brown jersey gone baggy over the summer and his autumnal hair. But hardly had the fuss ebbed a little but it rose to a scream again. Eugene's presence was demanded on a platform. When he asked his mother if she'd meet him for a coffee in Novodmitrovskaya Street that was it – the boy was mad the poor woman decided – and Eugene was put into the mental hospital . . .

Alan's first time to see this mental hospital close-up was in autumn 1949 when the Virginia creeper was burgundy on it. In his long coat, tightly belted on him, he shuddered and paused outside the Victorian façade with the golden hands reading four on the black face of the clock in the overhead dome. He was visiting a relative. Alan returned to this mental hospital after his visit to Rome. This was not a Sunday afternoon outing. This time he was locked in with all the figures from history beside him: Elizabeth I, Shane O'Neill, Red Hugh O'Donnell. He craned out the iron bars on the avenue which he'd once walked up, a young school-teacher come to pay a call on an aunt who'd substituted chocolates for life . . .

Eugene was fascinated. Here was Cromwell's Connaught. Mrs O'Hearne from Clifden, a widow, who enjoyed conjugal relations with the Sacred Heart. She would have been left alone had she not put her knickers – sent by a sister from Birmingham – at the feet of the statue of the Sacred Heart in the church in Clifden. There was Chris Moylan, a bachelor from Belmullet, who indulged in orgies with angels on the barren, sea-blown plains of the Erris peninsula. He too would have been left alone had he not approached the parish priest; a hat held out in his hand, and Chris claiming that inside it was a phantom baby he conceived with an angel. More than anyone, Eugene enjoyed Cathleen MacNamara, also from Mayo, a parish priest's housekeeper who, on the death of the priest climbed into the gale buffeted four-poster bed alongside the priest and stayed there for a couple of days with the corpse, nibbling goldgrain. Now she distributed goldgrain, sent by relatives in Mayo, to grateful mongoloids and to old ladies still reeling after the effects of electric shock treatment.

There was one stained glass window in a dark crevice of the mental hospital and Eugene stood under it, in its blues and reds remembering. This was Cromwell's Connaught, a place of loneliness but of visions, a place of spinster women at remote doorways and of young seventy-year-old men cycling home from fairs, chocolate in their pockets and a letter from a brother who'd left and gone to Brooklyn and escaped. The nurses spoke of a man from Athlone who came here on day visits, a teacher, 'Shakespeare' they called him. Only afterwards did Eugene make the connection.

His mother in her fur coat brought him chocolates and pathetic red carnations. His father, drooping a little, hat in hand, looked impressed by his mad son. Snow came and on a Sunday afternoon the inmates fired snowballs at one another on the pitch where local young men usually played football at this time of week, the old ladies decked out in long coats and wellingtons. Eugene watched from behind iron bars. He was enjoying this place so much his mother noticed and he was removed.

Looking at Brian Jones's picture on a record sleeve in a shop window early in December, Eugene suddenly felt someone behind him. He looked around. I had returned from England. Our little house by the woods was about to be sold. And I took a week off work to be there, to light a few last fires. In the blue twilight, snow about to fall, in my grimy brown left-over coat, I'd never known anyone to have changed as much as Eugene McDermott. His freckles had expanded – from fear maybe. I asked him to my home.

On the way, I slipped into a shop near the hospital and purchased a two litre bottle of red wine which I proudly bore away. In the house I rekindled the fire. Red berries craned in from outside. We did not talk of sad things, but laughed. Drunk, we both slept on a haggard eiderdown – pigeon feathers emerged from it at intervals – still in our coats by the fire. In the morning when I woke I examined a patch of stone floor on which I'd once observed a ladybird taking a promenade in sunlight which fell then exactly as it was falling now except that it was summer then.

[11]

Alan wasn't sure when history became sexual for him, but he did know that, after writing his leaving certificate essay on Red Hugh O'Donnell, Red Hugh – the young man who died in Simancas of poison – merged with his sexual fantasies. Red Hugh O'Donnell became a companion.

Alan was wearing a clean white shirt when he finished his history examination. He emerged into the daylight. The summer would be long. At the end of summer hopefully he'd be travelling to Dublin. A Christian Brother, in attendance without a cane, made a gruff remark. Alan walked by the Shannon. It was a grey blustery afternoon – at moments there was sunshine – the waves chopped. That night Alan had an imagining of Red Hugh O'Donnell sleeping in his arms and as the weeks went by the imaginings became heated and sexual. The summer was lazy in Athlone. Girls stood about between games of tennis. The lavatory walls were splayed with graffiti 'I want to stick my thing up a little boy's bum.' Rain urinated on the rugby changing-rooms. There the graffiti from last season were different. 'Bernie McLoughlin has a hairy ball.' After tennis hops bankers' daughters disappeared to the Shannon with boys about to go to college. Spinsters peered out of windows, their biscuit-tin eyes agleam with horror. Nuns accompanied one another for walks by the hosiery factory. Hitler was having it off with Deanna Durbin according to one piece of graffito in town, slashed in chalk across a grey stone wall by the Shannon. Alan and Red Hugh became more intimate. Red Hugh O'Donnell had a face of beaten copper – freckles washed into one another on it. His hair was carrot colour; his nipples languid. Girls waited in vanilla tennis shelters between showers. Alan touched Red Hugh's twig-like arms. A nun ran after a marshmallow blown away in the breeze. Alan kissed Red Hugh's lips. A Protestant woman's dalmatian made love to a fox terrier in the street. After love-making Alan looked into Red Hugh's eyes and Red Hugh became modern, became contemporary. He wore a polka dotted dickie bow and he performed a Fred Astaire-type tap-dance. The Sacred Heart reproached Alan in the church. The only time Alan actually made love was with a priest. The priest had taken his little penis. Alan wasn't sorry. Religion joined with sexuality and Alan saw sexuality as a way to God. But he was without a consort. Just a fantasy one. And over the summer – girls looking at him on the bridge – Red Hugh talked to Alan more and more, about his childhood in Donegal, a pet chicken he'd had, his father's feasts – cow's entrails roasted in cow skin – a nun he'd made love to in a buttercup field by the Atlantic. And Alan in turn spoke of himself and, as he spoke, his fantasy image disappeared and Alan found himself admitting he'd wanted to make love to his brothers, wanted to make love to rugby players but all the time really just sought a brother, a male companion. There'd been a dearth. Alan had been alone. So sexual fantasy had been substituted and now sexual fantasy seemed a key; a key to what? One day Alan realized. Children. He kept seeing the beginnings of a certain image of himself as a child but the image eluded him.

Girls made love for the first time that summer. Young men rowed on the Shannon. The working classes disappeared to England and the skirts of nuns rose. When harvest time was just culminating in the hills above the Shannon, Red Hugh O'Donnell returned to Alan's dreams but this time the relationship was different, more cerebral, more sober. War was just about to break out. The relationship now was a relationship between two young intensely intellectual seminarians, but no less passionate. They discussed the surfeit of world problems. Their own problems were somewhow left behind. But once or twice Alan did mention childhood, the way childhood haunts. Why should childhood haunt just before the outbreak of the Second World War? Why the image of a child when millions of people are about to die? The Virginia creeper turned colour on the hosiery factory; Alan's examination results came and his acceptance by the teacher's training college in Dublin. Alan's brothers shuffled in the night and Alan's mother found Alan naked on his bed, holding his penis, the day the war broke out. A lady who made masks gave some to children and the children paraded over the bridge on the Shannon, ghoul masks on their faces, white sheets on their bodies. Alan said goodbye to Red Hugh O'Donnell because he knew he was going. 'You kept me company.' The first rugby matches were played and Red Hugh metamorphosed into a woman or disappeared totally. That was the end of adolescence, the day Red Hugh went, but his memory of him expanded: an unreal young man, who substituted for a real adolescent companion, his hair a passionate carrot colour, a medieval monk-like cropping on it, and his eyes the green of the map of Ireland at school. Alan got the train to Dublin but a memory accompanied him, a shadow, and the only direction of this shadow would be art, the making of things from the sexual fantasy of a summer, the resolution of negation into construction, of an abyss of loneliness into words on a page. A priest sat alongside Alan on the train and Alan thought of that time with the priest in bed when he'd been nine; afterwards wondering at the way the sacramental joined with the lewd and the debased. The red skirts of altar boys danced attendance on a priest in Alan's mind and the train tore across the Midland plains of Ireland to Dublin.

On Christmas Eve, Cherine sipped tea in our flat, my mother suddenly flung her arms in the air. She grabbed a coat, rushed out to the telephone kiosk on the road outside the enclosure of blocks of flats and within minutes we were being borne by a black cab man to Westminster Cathedral where we joined some floral cloth garbed boys and girls who could have been the first hippies, mods, rockers, Irish charwomen, what looked like an African princess, her embroidered headdress high above her head. 'And it came to pass in those days, that there went out a decree from Caesar Augustus, that all the world should be taxed.' My mother bowed as the cardinal blessed the crowd. Later she sat up in the flat telling dirty jokes and drinking thimblefuls of whiskey as the first children ventured on the streets of White City.

In the new year – it was about February – Cherine and I went to a party. It was held in a flat on the first floor of a house in Davies Street off Oxford Street. Cherine, now heavily pregnant, still in her short black dress, on top of a lot of alcohol, took her first whiff of marijuana. The tableau of a town wavered, emerald creeping at the feet of grey spires, a crystalline river encircling the emerald. Cherine climbed on a table and waving her arms above her pregnant stomach declaimed to a gathering of actors and cosmetics experts about the town, in her words, 'that tried to do her in'. She enumerated the wrongs or imaginary wrongs it had committed against her family; its refusal to grant them meagre encampment space on the fair Green in the eighteenth century, the inhospitable way the corpses of her family dead were received in the workhouse during the Famine, the banishment to Flea Lane when her family decided to settle – fleas, wasps, insects rubbed into their wounds – the disdain with which they were held when they subsequently entered new walks of life. It was a town which had drowned her mother, parented her child, tried to commit genocide against her teenage body. But she'd go back Cherine declared, black hair falling in anger over her white forehead – two effete young men whose buttocks were buttressed by tight jeans exchanged comments in high pitched voices – she'd go back and claim the hereditary rights of her child, and, if she had to scrabble against the grey walls, reclaim her own historical dignity. Cherine fell sobbing into my arms, recalling the town as she'd seen it after she'd made love to me, way below her, the spires against the light of dawn and the medieval river mirroring the dawn, pink stripes gesticulating in the sky as if for the first time. Holding her, I walked Cherine to her bus, the two of us tottering a little, rouge rubbing into the rain blackened pavements of Oxford Street . . .

'Sabina where are you going?' Once a relative of Cherine's had stood on a veranda in the mid-west of America. The sun was going down. It was autumn. Inside, a man, her friend, made a potato dish, potatoes mixed with cheese and sour cream. She just had a frail, pink, New York purchased cardigan on her shoulders. The American flag fluttered in the garden above pumpkins; at the bottom of the garden, next to the cornfields, apples lay, orange lanterns, some ignited into decay. For the first time months of moving made sense to her, one event separating itself from another: making love to an old farmer at home; grabbing his money, leaving home; standing on a station platform, laurels of memory about her; getting the boat from Liverpool, a stop-over at Cobh, her relatives on the pier, some choking the pier with ponies and traps; East 43rd Street, the sky-scrapers against the furnaces of midsummer sunsets; staying with a great-uncle in Philadelphia; photographs of ancient tinker caravans, mounds of horse shoes on their fronts; the bus journey west; Mennonites singing songs of praise against the industrial citadels of the Mid-West; Arriving here, a brief stop-over, a love-affair, a respite in the midst of turmoil. Instead of going in, Sabina Finnerty began to walk on, past the flag, down the slope. She hesitated at the sty, then crossed into the fields. She did not think to go far but gradually as the cornfields swept about her she became mesmerized by them and kept going. 'Sabina, you're a tinker and will always remain a tinker ' 'Sabina, take that filthy plaster off your leg.' 'Sabina, go back to the bogs where you belong and look after your mangy cows.' The convent where she heard these insults was situated at the top of the street. The geography of the town she was from asserted itself among the cornfields: doorways, town-hall, fair Green, trees, yes, trees piled on limestone grey, piecing together the spring. 'You'll not come to any good, you slut.' 'Sabina, was it you who soiled the latrine this morning?' 'Sabina, you look such a miserable ungainly thing.' Suddenly Sabina found herself on a hill with a view of Iowa about her. Lakes, sea, varying shades of corn surrounded her. An ocean of corn rocked at her feet. Her miniature figure in its pastel pink cardigan was lost among the waves. 'O Lord how perfect thy works are.' The same rat-like nun who treated her to insults at school informed her class about all the unrequited harvests of Ireland and now, in the middle of this abundance, Sabina wanted to return to the town, where even the dead seemed oppressed, and bring them a bit of this moment – like a chalk dog in the window of an up-to-date tinker's caravan – but she knew she had to go on, through the Arctic sunset, past the distant country and western electricity of westward going trucks, through a barrier created by history, experience and atrophied personal deeds, to give birth at last from her life, to bring to the silver screen all the pain and loss of the place she was from. But whatever attended her mission – success or failure – she knew she'd always have this moment, this plenitude, clouds like fragments of the North Pole dying away and a silent music coming from the corn. Why had she been privileged to escape, why had she been chosen, why had the role been levied on her – why had her life been delivered from the lives like skeletons being pressed under slabs, bony hands protruding into the verdure – she could not even picture the town now alongside this peace, but before she could solve these problems the cold became too much for her and she started back, pulling her cardigan tighter about her, with each step knowing she was leaving behind a space she had not prepared for in her life, a space where there was no ambition, just tranquillity, the uneasy lives from home – a hooligan youth with a voluminous quiff of black hair on his forehead who was drowned in the local river, an ancient tinker woman often seen at the fairs – alongside her in a prayer. A triad of candles waited for her on the table, lit. She enthroned herself like a queen, removing her cardigan to show her arms in a white sleeveless blouse, poising her arms on the white tablecloth, her black hair rolling on her shoulders, looking ahead, past the Stars and Stripes gone mad now, the glimmering pumpkins, the fallen apples like illuminated sentries, to a corner in the fields beyond, which was not quite devoured by darkness, where the ghost of a girl seemed to flail her arms in happiness.

[13]

Eugene sauntered home after the night he'd spent with me as if there'd been nothing unusual in spending the whole night out. The sun was shining, the sky blue and under glistening branches of oak trees his hair radiated stripes of auburn and gold. He hugged himself into his long coat, hands supine in his deep pockets. There was a gleam of happiness, of mischief in his face. It was this attitude of nonchalance which disturbed his mother most. Eugene was put back into the mental hospital where he was supposed to remain except for the days immediately surrounding Christmas. A few days before the New Year Eugene ran away.

Cars streamed towards the station, red gashes. It was already dark or nearly dark. Eugene trudged through the slush, money in his pocket an aunt had given him. The Midland plains were occasionally illumined by cottage windows, and snow, threatening to renew itself, flung past in flakes.

Dublin was a wash of neon. Eugene headed towards the Liffey. A spiral of faces and lights writhed about him which became a single writhing phantom. This pillar of fire accompanied Eugene to the Liffey. Sometimes a single face seemed to disengage from this pillar like a spark and vie for Eugene's attention, but he was in the thrall of a notion. All moments are haunted by other moments this notion stated; there is an ancestry to our every act, people, faces behind it; this was not a new concept to his life but it seemed singularly appropriate tonight when the face of one young man more than any other established itself in the Dublin night, but before Eugene could ask the details – the young man's name, where he was from – the face faded. Other people had been to this country Eugene decided, maybe they'd failed in their bid for it but at least they'd left the route open. What this country was he did not know, but he was by the Liffey and a single flake of snow flew past and the collar of his coat was pulled up over a green silk tie, given him by the aunt who'd given him the money, loosely tied on a white shirt, hieroglyphics of coloured threads scintillating in the tie, his hair agleam and, as far as Eugene was concerned, his lips shivering with the cold, Dublin becoming the hastening, the universal city, neon wobbling in the depths of the water below, he was dipping into the same fire as others had done before him.

Alan slouched across the Vatican Square, his dark suit drooping on him, the effects of last night's drinking still in his head. Gold dots stood back and peered at him. Nuns paired in conversation. Alan too bordered on another world, with him one of his own creation. Nuns transformed into cardinals in ruminative red, gentlemen in cocked hats, turquoise rings on their hanging fingers. It was the century when Galileo bantered with Barberini, when Queen Christina, the snow-queen, was drawn by white horses into Rome, when the sacking of Mantua was still in tremulous whispers on people's lips. Lorcan O'Mahony strode across the Vatican Square, confident in his scarlet cloak and big boots he could compete with the Michelangelo males

131

within. A particularly cantankerous looking cardinal glowered at him, his soutane not the expected brightness but the colour of ox tongue. From outside the square a girl selling apples desperately tried to catch Lorcan's attention, one russet apple squelched in her outheld hand like excrement, her little body hunched up, on her head a knitted cap with variously coloured diamond patterns, a basket of apples alongside her. Her brothers and sisters, more sedate, sold rice and mousetraps, and one young man played a galliard on a guitar. But of late Alan was getting sick of his historical creations; he wanted to move on, change, shed old identity. That month, November, under the statue of Giordano Bruno in Campo de' Fiori on a moonlit night, drunk, he encountered a boy in a salmon jersey who did not look unlike a statue himself, his arms folded, a solemn composure in his face. The day's marigolds and carnations were trodden into the cavities between wet cobbles at the boy's feet. Alan made an absurd remark about the moon, gesturing remonstratingly to it and to his surprise the boy replied in English. Alan asked him home. The statue consented.

Simon – the boy's name – had spent a fatherless childhood in Trastevere; his mother had been killed by a stray bullet during the German retreat in 1944, the unsuspecting woman wandering down a street when she was caught by a German soldier's farewell gesture. He'd picked up his English, sometimes perfect, sometimes flawed, depending, as Alan was to discover, on what he had to say, from American soldiers whom he approached for chocolate, magnetised by the oblong, upheld bars of chocolate, a terrified animal. 'Thrush' the American soldiers had called him either because of his upthrusting hair or because of some obscene connotation.

In his hotel room, drunken, Alan began mauling the boy. 'I've got to go,' Simon said. Alan asked, 'Please stay the night. Just sleep alongside me.' They didn't just sleep alongside one another. In the morning Alan stared at the wall, remembering a big, Victorian confessional in the church in Athlone and the sins it seemed to require; now he had embroidered sins to satiate this wardrobe-like edifice. Simon had gone for bread, cheese and wine with money Alan had given him and he returned, miraculously changed, in a blue-and-white striped T-shirt and hefty shorts.

Since the war Simon had survived on chocolate biscuits from American soldiers; clothes he'd picked up from Carmelite nuns and carnations for his lapel he'd procured from the museum gardens of Rome.

'You reech? You lonlee? You – mad?' Simon swathed his naked

body in a toga-like towel and appeared at the door for Alan's entertainment.

Immediately after the war Simon had scoured Rome for a home; ash heaps, rubbish dumps, the ruins of railway installations. Now he inhabited a mysterious lair with other boys who had the pearly glow of the blasts of Hiroshima and Nagasaki in their eyes.

'You are my fatheer, motheer, brotheer, seester.' That moment, in his arms, Simon could have been Alan's child.

At night in bed beside him, Alan had a body the colour of a beach transformed and scorched by a summer sun. 'Which way do you want eet?' Despite his initial hesitance – Alan had intimated a violence that Simon could not identify in the repertoire of his experience – Simon was a male prostitute. He gave his body the way Rome gave its ruins. He lay face down on the pillow. For a moment Alan didn't touch him. In the morning Alan walking back from the shop saw a gander, obviously up to mischief the previous night, rise into the narrow realm of light, shooed by an outraged woman. Alan sewed Simon's T-shirt, washed his filthy trousers as the boy still lay in bed. 'What are you theenking of?' Alan was sitting on his hunkers, staring at the wall. 'Nothing. Nothing.' As it was still early Alan went out. First he revisited Keats' grave, then the graves of O'Neill and O'Donnell. In fact he'd been thinking of Red Hugh O'Donnell, the companion of a summer, more real than the tennis playing boys and girls of Athlone, the landscape of his hair and the buttercup landscape of his home more real than the golf mounds which surrounded Athlone. 'Alan what are you thinking of?' his mother had asked him suspiciously. Alan at that moment was thinking of the constellation of freckles over Red Hugh's nose and the few sparse freckles over his white, languishing buttocks. At one point that summer two girls, intrigued by his reputation, tennis racquets hanging by their sides, stood on the bridge over the Shannon, staring at him as if he was Frankenstein. But he didn't notice. He was running naked with Red Hugh into the huge, oncoming Atlantic waves. 'What do you want?' the postmistress cum merchant of chocolate had snapped at him. Red Hugh O'Donnell, in a dinner jacket and bow-tie, was declaiming from a velvet couch a Gaelic dictum 'He who scatters gathers.' In an autumn of green, supine grapes and proficient gathering, in sunshine in an orange T-shirt over Keats' grave, or in the mildewed air around O'Neill's and O'Donnell's graves, Alan wondered at the conundrum of a summer, how an imaginary companion could have been more real than the people around him and world events. The sexual nature of his relationship with the boy intensified. In a cold, splashing shower

133

he held the truculent body of an adolescent boy, fingering the hardening dancer's chest. 'There was one sect of monks in Galway who defied Giovanni Battista Rinuccini and the sprite-faced cardinal hovered along by the ocean side steps, swept his cloak up High Market Street and outside this sect's chapel launched a hefty kick at the sacramental shins of an unsuspecting monk, guarding the chapel in his hood and gown.' 'General Munro, the puritan general, fled the Battle of Benburb without his wig, the squat little man galloping over the emerald of Tyrone, bald head gleaming after a shower.' 'The Moors had left Andalucia in 1609, but Lorcan when he arrived felt their grafted presence, old men smoking out of snake-like hoses, young girls walking across ceramic walls, bushels of grapes on their heads.' In an affair with a boy in Rome, Alan realized that his novel had, for the most part, evolved from a summer; all the historical annotations, all the obsessive particularising, had been an attempt not just to break with images that transfixed experience, but to break from an entire sense of stultifying national history, to create from it. But the attempt had reverberated upon itself. With this boy the sexual fantasy was still of a youth with carrot hair who had officially died in Simancas in 1602 but who had roamed the streets of Athlone one summer, dived into the Shannon, pulled on cigarettes outside the cinema, slipped into pubs with cherry coloured fronts to have a pint, leaving Alan outside. 'Once a man asked me if he could taste my meelk for 20,000 lira.' 'Lorcan moved towards Eleanor's breast, both of them on the stone floor, goose feathers falling into the open hearth, some straining on the lovers, a brook running through the kitchen, bringing brown mountain water and, when they were finished with their love-making, a lulling sense of mountain-tops and sheep as the two young people fell apart, staring at the rafters which all the time had been observing them, a partition of gold, of lace, of velvet between the young man and woman.' 'He took me to the Coliseum and did eet as I looked at the birds.' The boy's buttocks arched towards Alan. Alan held his waist from behind. 'I want to feel myself, body, chest, nipples, prick. I want to – to forget.' The boy turned towards Alan's chest, crying, a rivulet of semen between them. Later the boy asked Alan, who was lying on the floor against the wall, what he was thinking of. 'History,' Alan replied. The boy who was himself lying on the floor against the opposite wall looked baffled. History to him was old Jewish men being pulled out of church houses by their white hair, curfews, gladiatorial battles between snipers on bicycles and German soldiers, processions of hunger, ruins, the post-war parentlessness of the world.

The two young men went to a film, Buster Keaton. Afterwards they walked through Rome. The fountains, cobbled squares by moonlight charted the emotional topography of Dublin for Alan, sites where he'd furthered his education in life. Merrion Street in Maytime, converging on the Peppercannister, where a waif-like boy in his winter coat approached him and commiserated with him about the terribleness of war. Palmerston Park, also in Maytime, cricketing boys racing in white, where an old lady offered him a gratuitous basket of baby strawberries because, she said, she felt he'd relish them. Sandymount village where the trams stopped – there a dray horse had viciously kicked Alan in his efforts to pat the animal. Rathgar – in one of its prettified box-like cottages an elderly man had tried to seduce Alan. Alan and the boy ventured onto the spiral of streets leading to the Borghese Gardens. Alan was visited by moments of history, not the bleak ones, but happy, rich ones. Grace O'Malley, pirate Queen of Mayo, assailing the court of Elizabeth in Greenwich, in a green chieftain's cloak, her auburn, flowing hair sweeping past the carved oak wainscots as the ladies of the court gasped and the Queen rose, a little puff of henna. Honora, Lady Kerry, trespassing on the top of a mound, delicately holding her skirts, waiting for her lover, the fugitive Pierce Ferriter. Elizabeth, Lady Butler, ringing out notes on the harpsichord in her castle in County Kilkenny, miles of aspen avenues outside shaking to the music. The moon was full. Rome was cradled under the moon. From the Borghese Gardens Alan surveyed the city, a feast in the sky; a cartoon in a college textbook coming alive. beef being broiled in cow's hide, a mangy wolfhound whining at a long table, a man defecating to the side of the picture much as one would do a jig – his bottom perilously stuck out – a monk devouring a chicken leg, a lady smiling. 'Keep it to yourself when the moon is waxing, show it to the world when the moon is full, throw it away when the moon is waning.' Incongruously, afternoon tea advice from a Protestant lady outside Athlone returned. Tonight the moon was full. There was nothing in particular to show the world but there was a boy by Alan's side and cameos of history in his mind. Tonight history was a richness. History was a girl with a smile. She was compounded from many women in the corners of Irish history books; she had black hair, solemn white skin and she smiled in the sky, perfectly reflecting the world of a young man with black hair and its temporal glasses of red wine.

In an all-night café they drank coffee. An old man with hamster white hair stared at them from a chair. The proprietor patted the counter comfortably. On the juke-box the humming chorus from the end of the first part of the second act of *Madame Butterfly* played. Back in the hotel they stayed up all night. The boy sat opposite Alan. During the last few days, bit by bit, the boy had established himself as someone who looked Alan's age, an equal; someone you could set alongside Alan and not be disconcerted about the nature of their relationship. In a dark jacket and a polka-dotted tie picked up in a flea market, he reclined now. He was the brother Alan had always been looking for. From the belly of the hotel a clock ticked. The boy confronted Alan, dark hair slanting over his forehead, brunette eyes wondering. In the near silence winds conquered the cobwebs in the basements of Irish castles; Red Hugh O'Donnell's face took form out of the boy's face, chestnut hair, green eyes, features sieved with freckles. But it did not bring tableaux of snow ruffling in Donegal or snow battering against the dark walls of Dublin castle. It was a contemporary face. Alan recognised it as being part of himself, an inarticulated part, red gashes in the whites of the eyes; his own adolescence, a supine, abandoned thing. It was a face which was destined to recur and recur, like an historical character purgatorially revisiting some scene, until some pain was alleviated, until some knowledge was gained, until some memory was diminished. The boy continued staring at Alan. There was an apocalypse in those eyes. It was the end of summer in Athlone. Girls gathered their scarves around their necks on the bridge over the Shannon a few days after the war had broken out. Rat-grey Atlantic clouds scudded over. Red Hugh O'Donnell walked over that bridge, he too in a scarf, many coloured, one that always seemed incomplete but now that he was going, appeared fully woven. The face faded as slowly as it had come. But there was silence in the room. It was as if the boy had intercepted Alan's vision, had accosted the amount of imaginative possibilities being placed upon him. In the morning – a bottle of red wine on the table – Simon went to buy bread and cheese for breakfast. He never returned.

Early one morning just before Christmas, in a trattoria, Alan realized he had another novel inside him. This one he wouldn't lock in a drawer. This one he'd show to the world. But what would happen to the Lorcan O'Mahonys and the Eleanor O'Keefes? Would it be a denial of them? No they would pack their suitcases and move from one novel to another. By showing it to the world Alan would be able to grow at last, indulge in the many acts of the ordinary, pick the long black stripes of women's stockings from the floor after making love to the women, marry, have children. But first he'd have to go back. Early the previous summer as he'd crossed a field by the Shannon he'd nearly stumbled on a moment of childhood. Now, in a Roman trattoria sipping a cappuccino, he saw himself in the fogged window in a white shirt crossing a field by the Shannon, a smile on his lips, a vagary in his mind...

Eugene, by the Liffey, encountered a snowman for the second time in his life. The snowman had grown more elderly, a Charlie Chaplin hat on his head, spectacles on his nose, but he was no less jocose. 'Tonight history is a richness. To move on you've got to go back to the first innocence of history. To move on you've got to go back to childhood. I want to write more honestly, more directly but first I've got to go back and find the child in me who once wrote a poem about a snowman – a snowman who, although he rapidly melted, is perennial because a child wrote about him. I want to find a place in my emotions for that child. The snowman melts all around me now; it is grandiose as it melts; white sparks ignite and blow outwards – but it remains tacitly intact as it melts in a child's first, secure and healing vision.' The blackness of one person's night merged into blackness of another's.

Eugene was found in the morning sleeping beside a dustbin alongside which hot-house daffodils were on display late into the night, white scrolls at their necks. He was sent home and put back into the mental hospital. In May he was released, mainly because his mother wanted him to do examinations.

Sweat broke from unopened buds above him as he emerged. Eugene had changed, less lustre in his hair, in his freckles – they'd taken part of his brain, the sound of a train, the splash of neon – the path was laid out for him, miles of suburban, mountain-side houses but he was still determined to resist that course, whatever further effort that might cost.

[14]

Cherine's baby started coming at the end of March. In my red jacket I stood outside. Only the intermittent cigarettes connected the ikons; green trees, lady-like waterfalls, young soldiers' eyes. 'The child of a town.' The cigarettes made an island of smoke above me and in this island I could see all the people I'd become; they waltzed, they drank wine at wedding feasts, they stood before cameras in studios. It was another country. I did not feel real. I knew where I was born. I knew the country I'd moved to. But beyond that there were just connecting impressions. Cherine's screams penetrated the cloud of smoke. My mind took refuge anywhere but in the fact that it was my child which was being delivered.

When the baby was born – a girl – Cherine, as planned, sneaked out of a ground-floor hospital window with her suitcase. I was waiting outside. First we had coffees in a café. In Victoria Station as I dallied over a magazine Cherine tugged me on. They'd be after us. On my small earnings we were heading south; Morocco, Spain. Cherine's scarfed head inclined in sleep against the window of the train. The baby could be adopted. A farmer peered drowsily into the train from a spade top. The English countryside was coming to life. Edmund Spenser's Munster once looked like this. I pulled myself up. I was thinking of that novel again. In Dover we baulked – it was mainly Cherine – and we spent some weeks among honeymooning couples. Elderly couples moped among their memories. Coloured lights festooned the pier-side. Young sailors threw lascivious glances at both of us. Pop songs crooned incessantly over holocausts of chips, 'Silence is Golden', 'There's a hush all over the World'. Cherine's hair was in a ponytail. Its shining black scintillated against the weightless Easter blue skies. Her hand slipped easily into mine. There was a stubborn energy in that hand and her nose was suddenly snub and freckled. Her eyes darted to the sea. There was no need to go further. Away from Ireland she'd encountered her own worth. Our landlady treated us as she would the most suitable of honeymooning couples, smilingly presenting us with banquets of topped eggs, their gold flowing, until inadvertently one morning she heard Cherine's description on the radio. That temporarily put an end to running for us.

Aftermath

'The first thing I remember about Sainte Marie is the skies, early morning skies. Skies you felt you could blow away. A little girl, I walked along those beaches in early morning, encountering a seashell, a bottle, a gypsy. Sometimes a dark, sudden gypsy man would rise from behind a sand-dune. They were the monsters and the kings of my childhood, the gypsy men.' Denise when small would frequently wander into a church in Sainte Marie where Saint Sarah, patroness of gipsies, was always rigid. It was as if Saint Sarah's explosive blue eyes were trying to communicate something to the little girl. It was as if there were messages in those eyes for the little girl. The carmine, doll's lips tried to whisper, the veil tried to move. But nothing came out. After the war the messages were only too clear. Saint Sarah was different. She'd had a vivisection in a Nazi concentration camp. There were memorial anemones at her feet.

The war had been a caged time for Denise; a small house in Vichy. Her bald factory owner father stumbled about in memories of a languorous mansion beside the Bois de Boulogne in Paris. Denise was no longer the little girl her father would take by the hand in Ile de la Cité on days Notre Dame looked as if it would take off like a balloon. She was growing, a stripling; her sisters jealous of her. Vichy was watching men annex the ace of diamonds; Vichy was black penitential dresses, shoes and stockings. After the war, while attending school in a town where Saint Bernadette was laid out like a fish, Denise returned to Sainte Marie with her family, to their house there. The eyes of gypsy women were silent and hollow with horror.

An amusement arcade had sprung up by the sea and the girls spent most of their time there; there were young men, splashes of sun on the dartboards and in the dark, game eyes of young men. And there was also brash music. But occasionally, Denise took leave of the music and wandered – her father at home muttering to the gold-fish, Christian, Mark and Athinéa; her mother brandishing a tray of bowls with paprika covered potatoes in them for visitors. Denise was the one who most often disconnected herself from her sisters; her life was a mixture, a balance; revels and then sojourns with herself. There were songs which stated this duality for her.

On one of her wanderings she met an old Irish tinker lady; the lady's story built like an ikon. Denise came with bottles of cooking wine and little phial of liqueur from their pantry at home to encourage her. And gradually Denise saw it, the old lady's life. She'd arrived in Marseille on a barge, if you were to believe her, after marrying a French gypsy. Her date of birth was 1875. She was born, thrown into existence, on the roads of Galway. She'd beheld Parnell's beatific face, being held up by her father. She'd camped by big houses, under mountains, in soggy flat fields. The names of pubs and big stores on the main streets of Irish towns floated in her head like coloured banners. But she'd parted from her native country with a degree of bitterness. 'Les gens, ils crachaient sur nous.'

The merry-go-rounds in Sainte Marie de la Mer crazed against the sunsets, the people juggled laughter, Denise's skirts and thighs swooned to young men. She danced on an empty floor with a young man. But the experience of this place by the sea was balanced; her adolescence was also an encounter with the gypsies, the gypsies of Hungary, Bulgaria, Poland and with a solitary Irish tinker woman, fond of cooking wine, who made you hear the music of her country, who articulated the vowels of her country and who drank, paradoxically, to drown the sense of it. But in Sainte Marie, Ireland became real for Denise; not as a faraway place but because it was a parallel with her experience of the war; every image the old lady invoked was splintered by diversity, whether an image of rocks or carnival lights, every emotion was a duality. An old lady, bereft of an alleged husband, played a tin-whistle in an abandoned house in Sainte Marie, fingered a bottle of wine, spat on the ground, and commenced her prayers.

Denise did not think much about Ireland during her years at the Sorbonne. In a midget tomato coloured Peugeot she flared around Paris. Her head was enwrapped in a scarf and her legs dangled, like a blue-bottle's in tight slacks. It was another decade. The mists were greyer and more gregarious. Lovers wound in and out of Denise's little flat and her life – streaming up a narrow stairway – some finding it difficult to extricate themselves. Her father urged her towards professorships but, her initial studies at the Sorbonne over, she travelled in a personal heat; Czechoslovakia, Poland, but found herself back in Switzerland, dark glasses over her eyes, reflecting the mountains. Wherever she went her father's wealth drew her back. Denise sailed down the snowy precipices on skis. She still saw far-off goals, smoke whisking in India, but she could not reach it. Her life was a collection, a pyramid of clothes, drinks. She wanted to excel herself, discover the little person within, give birth from herself but the apparatus of wealth was too powerful. Instead of studying to be a professor as her father wanted, she dyed her hair red and married – a diplomat – deserting France for England. There she wore a black dress and foraged in Tibetan cookbooks. Separation from her husband meant moving out of one house on Holland Park Avenue into another. She was living in the second house when she met me. I revived something; an old lady on a beach in the Camargue, a day in Arles when she laughed with an adolescent vagabond, watching him mime Charlie Chaplin as she sat on the steps of a house.

I was working in a bookstore off the King's Road, mainly wheeling books around. Cherine had long vacated my life. She'd stormed out on a rainy day. Our baby was dumped in Hampstead. Cherine had taken up evening studies, trying to be a hairdresser or a cosmetics expert, anything that would entitle her to be middle-class and return to Ireland. She owed it to her ancestry to be middle-class. Her hair was in a bun on top of her head – a little piece of confectionery. She was dressed all in black, black coat, black stockings, as if mourning something, someone. She hardly glanced behind so professional was her new gait.

I wore a skimpy red jersey even on cold days. My hair was cut shorter. Their new life suited my parents. Denise was the French woman with red hair and in a black dress who pottered for hours about the shop, secluding herself in the dark basement with its dictionaries and annuals. That's how we encountered. We were usually the only ones there. 'The Irish boy,' she called me. She addressed queries about books to the trace of Irish accent in my voice though I was only the barrow boy and not supposed to know these things. One lunchtime I bumped into her in a café. Waving a solitary black glove, the other glove on, she remonstrated about Ireland. But it was not the Irish boy but the adolescent in me that made her invite me home.

Her home was a sea of new things, red bed drapes, fake leopard skin, elephant ivory. She watched as I wondered. She made chamomile tea and made certain intimate confessions to me, certain intimate divulgences. I was nervous and fled the red reflections.

But Denise, soon after, came into the shop as if there'd been a robbery in her home and imperiously issued an invitation to lunch on a day I'd have off. She floated away. My mother noted verbally the oil in my hair as I made my way out that morning.

Denise treated me as an honoured guest; we ate her Indonesian cooking. Afterwards she wanted me to tell her all, all about Ireland, my experiences there, how I came to be here in England, but as I continued with my autobiography her hand began wandering to a forlorn looking book.

It was not me that eventually made love to Denise but my body, the frail instrument of my chest. It was what I was supposed to do. My body rippled over hers on an expansive bed. Denise bought me a dark suit; I purchased for myself a white Italian shirt; I had a green silk tie. I had another role. I was Denise's young man. No one ever asked me my name at parties, what country I was from. It was sufficient to check my features from behind, my tumbled hair. Hiroshima clouds of marijuana behind me I wandered to the precipice of parties. I had arrived in a city I always sensed I'd come to, but there was a parallel city in my mind, a city of sewers, of fogs. I was wandering through a maze of sewers, lost.

'Where have you been? The Folies Bergères?' my mother asked. Apparently I'd picked up a slight French accent.

One night I encountered a woman in black in the city of sewers. She asked me the way to the solicitors. When I pointed a direction she declared 'A thousand blessings on you.' Earlier that autumn I'd caught sight of a riot in Northern Ireland doing a drunken jig on the corner of a television screen.

Denise had me sit on the edge of her bed and gave me tuition in her life; it seemed important to her to tell me how her husband had made love to her – how many times a day – how fat and repulsive his belly had been, how expansive and jaundiced his underpants had been.

In the city of sewers I met Eugene McDermott. I asked him how he was. He was studying for his final examinations at school.

The riots had played out in Paris, in Berlin; Denise tucked her arm into mine on Holland Park Avenue as we walked over riots of leaves and through disturbances of dust.

Red peppers were always about to burst from their frail skins in Denise's flat; the story of her life forever for the telling, a spindle of yarns on a bed-side.

Someone turned up the volume in London; the music had become louder. Film producers, actors touched me from behind on my shoulder.

Tanks and guns crept into the city of sewers. My hand stumbled for Radio Luxemburg. The lights of citadels of other council flats outside were reassuring and the pop pin-ups inside. Before Christmas carnations were growing in this city.

144

A reef passed tremblingly between people; there were white horses in the drugs, white horses and insistent, slimy Connemara castles.

One night the music was so loud Denise and I just danced, facing one another on an empty floor, wriggling like elastic things, walloping the air, the whole of Holland Park Avenue gradually coming to see us on the top storey of one of their houses.

I was a body, chest, nipples, prick. Denise informed me I had saccharine, edible nipples and our love-making became easier after that. But there was still the city of sewers in my mind, red carnations in it.

At Christmas I attended midnight Mass with my mother at Westminster cathedral. My hands lingered on top of one another in front of my grey sportscoat. The cardinal bestowed his benevolences on us.

January; London was a city of fog. One night near a block of Chelsea flats a woman asked me in the greyness and the blackness where the Thames was. I wondered, was she going to throw herself in?

In the New Year Denise spoke voraciously of travel; she could see her erstwhile India and Sri Lanka again. But as the New Year travel brochures poured in she settled for something less. And she was going to take me with her. The brochures made a portfolio in her lap; she sat inanimately. Over the next few months I visited the blue skies, the blue seas many times through the brochures.

In July, Denise and I comforted one another at the memorial concert for Brian Jones in Hyde Park where Mick Jagger inaudibly mumbled 'Weep no more for Adonis is not dead'; in a plain orange smock Denise had plonked herself among the myriad younger floral smocks.

Late August, just before we left England, I ventured into Holland Park one evening; young men intently played sitars on the ground, their minutely curled hair aureoles of light, the music of one clambering into the music of another and raising the gentle roof of autumn leaves; the young men and their attendant women waiting until last light, these Ranters, Diggers, Levellers, Anabaptists, whatever.

In France we hired a car. Denise kept her life story going. The billboards fell away from one another into the night, place-names; Fontainebleau, Dijon, Orange. In Sainte Marie de la Mer Denise discovered that the gypsies now wore hippie clothes and that the sea had changed colour.

We were nearly arrested for calling an Italian conductor a capitalist on a train. The train swung south. In Rome I was in Alan Mulvanney's city. Denise and I generally went separate ways. I walked and walked. Little boys tossed kicks at soccer balls. Ganders rose into the narrow illumination in alleyways. I was reconstructing something. I was nearly catching up on something; the head of a boy, red-haired. I visited Keats' grave and the graves of O'Neill and O'Donnell. Without Denise I sat on the Spanish Steps. White horses pulled in bearing Keats' carriage; a priest's version of Rome. Alan Mulvanney crossed the Piazza di Spagna; my own version of Rome. This once had been a city of sewers. In a café near the Spanish Steps, a Dutchman told me how after the liberation of Rome, when Keats' house had been locked up for years, a young Jewish American soldier was posted to it. One day the proprietress crept up the stairs to the unlit room where Keats had died to find the young soldier crying. Disconnecting yarns. I tried to tell Denise the story but she was busy putting make-up on her face in front of a narrow ungenerous mirror in a small hotel. Beside Denise I dreamt of the city of sewers again; Alan in the red, black lined, short-sleeved shirt he'd worn in Rome was walking alongside me. He was trying to tell me something. He was trying to warn me of something, but the crying of women in the distant hill-side catacombs was too much. I woke. In the morning in the hotel lounge Denise and I interviewed warrior hippies back from fracas with police, and jails in distant countries of drugs and wraith-like mountains.

A gull dipped over the azure early morning contours of Corfu. The woman beside me, looking with anxiety from the boat, was a stranger.

We burrowed ourselves into sleeping bags on the beaches of Greek islands; in the mornings we gathered the carcasses of our picnics and delivered them to appropriate spots. It was getting colder.

On a beach under Delphi I tried to tell Denise about Alan; under a mythic mountain I tried to tell her about myth, how a person you had never met could dominate your life, but she, crouching in her smock, grown haggard now on the beach either couldn't comprehend or was too distracted by an unruly strand of hair which she tried unsuccessfully to discipline with her right hand.

Back in London I wandered further to the precipices of parties. This time I was more daring in the drugs I took with me to these precipices. I was more liberal in the colours I allowed to cascade around me. Rats stumbled out of a gutter on Holland Park Avenue, grappling the nearby big, untidy, golden leaves. They pattered along Holland Park Avenue, singling out supermarkets for annihilation. An army of rats waltzed nearer the party. I screamed. An ambulance heard my scream and rushed noiselessly over the golden leaves. Its red light threw its arms around tree trunks. I could hear a language again, not the language of Alan's novel but the language which surrounded it, the people, the places, the silence that surrounded Alan's life, work and intended works. My scream subsided into silence in a South London mental hospital.

[2]

A woman confronts the head of Oliver Plunkett in a church in Drogheda, Ireland. Behind glass the head looks all pulp, red and blue. The woman is grey-haired, middle-aged. For years she has kept Oliver Plunkett's portrait in her room, well away from the double bed she shares with her husband, Oliver Plunkett's hair long, grey, wavy – a cavalier's hair – a look of alert holiness on his face above a maroon cassock against the troubled maroon and purple storm clouds of Ireland. For years she's prayed for the canonization of Oliver Plunkett. Oliver Plunkett, then Archbishop of Armagh, was hanged by the British at Tyburn in 1681. She has urged that canonization on mother-of-pearl beads inherited from her mother who in turn had prayed for this canonization on these beads. Soon the woman's request is to be granted. Oliver Plunkett is to be made a saint by the pope.

Mrs. McDermott joins a procession outside which is about to move off in preparation for the imminent canonization. Most of those gathered for the procession are women, middle-aged like Mrs. McDermott. In their flashing turkey blues and their starched white, they cackle as if they're girls at a dance. The difference with Mrs. McDermott is that she is alone. Either she could get no one to come with her or she has chosen to come alone. It is a fine day in early June. She wears a white lamb's wool cardigan. She carries a shining black handbag her husband gave her last Christmas which she exploits for the first time. As the procession moves off she looks imminently disconcerted and lonely. A nearby television camera captures her loneliness and her misplacement for the whole of Ireland to see.

'Faith of our fathers living still'. The procession moves under the churches and the high situated industrial citadels. The troubled graffiti on the factory walls speak of the nearby North of Ireland. Little girls stare blissfully at the colours and the varicose veins. As

147

Mrs. McDermott walks she takes the opportunity, now that a strand of meaning has emerged from her life, from the telling of her beads, to ponder her life.

She lives now in an age different from the one she was born in. She was born into a world of water, swans and sisters. There were cows, calves, bonhavs, the occasional calf dithering on its ballerina legs, selected for a blue ribbon. 'Hail Queen of Heaven.' Mrs. McDermott cycled, fed animals, walked in swamping fields. She lifted her skirts above yellow cabbage seed. She confronted the wild Easter Shannonside clouds. She thought to be a nun and a martyr but she fell in love and – for the first time in years, as she celebrates the imminent canonization of Blessed Oliver Plunkettt – she allows her mind to dwell on carnal love, to see the images of carnal love, the genitals, the nipples – the summer warts, all pus, on shirtless arms, that tell of genitals and nipples. She remembers the lips of a young man who remarked on her lips. Among the varicose veins, she remembers how sturdy he was and how educated he was and that he knew all the solicitors in the county. 'Star of the Sea, pray for the wanderer, pray for me.' She recalls with delight and bitterness her affair. Franco got him; he was given to Spain. The bishops, the priests, the sacristans murdered him. She would never have dreamt before that she was capable of such an admission, but here among the mardi gras nuns, among the women and the milky monks in brown striding gowns she realizes anything goes – as at a marriage ceremony the occasion soars to the head and makes you dizzy. Mrs. McDermott, almost joyfully, almost drunkenly, realizes why she'd quickly buried her relationship with the boy – it had been a contumely against her fathers. All these years it had been a darkness but now it is taken from the darkness. Breezes blow in from the Irish Sea. Mrs. McDermott rivets ahead. 'Lord make me an instrument of thy peace.' She had rejected a part of herself and moved over the bridge on the Shannon in a farm Ford.

The west of Ireland did not bring her the promised 'mountains of pound notes'. It did bring her a little prosperity, two children. The children were always at loggerheads with one another. Now they live in different countries to one another. The daughter's head dips when the son's name is mentioned. The son rarely writes. Mrs. McDermott takes little walks, peeping over riverside walls to see alcoves of new daffodils in spring. She rarely talks to other women. Her rosaries are profuse. She has a special relationship with the local nuns. You could say they have made her an honorary nun. She and her husband take trips to Galway. In Salthill she picks out goldgrain from her bag as she sips a half pint of Guinness. The summer girls go by. And she and her husband return to the small town and its street. But today she is alone and she perceives the zoo of her life – her brother with his mug ears, a priest from long ago who stalked the fields in wellingtons and urinated openly on rosebushes, pulling up his cassock.

At the end of the procession the women kneel among the flowers and repeat the Our Father in Irish. 'Ar n-athair atá ar neamh Go deifer d-anam Go dtaga do riach.' Mrs. McDermott has no Irish, but her lips visibly move on another prayer, a cascade of prayer; her life is a spiral today. Childhood, adolescence, young womanhood and old age – childhood again. Again she can see the clouds, the buttercups, again the wild teasing Shannonside clouds. History is part of her prayer; the history of her times, de Valera, the Second World War, economic growth, the Northern troubles. The more ancient history of Ireland, the hanging of bishops. She remembers why she is here and looks to a darkening cloud and is purgatorial and not joyful again. But the doleful ikons of other women rise against the sky and the homing planes.

Long after the prayer is over the Gaelic syllables reverberate; they follow women to the Wimpy bars and the waiting buses.

On impulse, instead of taking the train to Dublin Mrs. McDermott gets on a red bus and visits the grave of her oldest sister in a cemetery in the nearby hilly countryside. She has not been here for years. She approaches tremulously. She is disturbing an old self, a girl in a dance dress. The glass dome reflects her. Mrs. McDermott wants to pray but the moment makes a temporary collapse of emotion, makes a momentary atheist out of her. Then she rises to the occasion and addresses her sister. She wants to talk of tastes they shared, tastes for madeira cake, partly pink, partly yellow, tastes for potatoes in a pan, gurgitating country butter. But instead she talks of things that happened to her since, her husband, children. She remembers her oldest sister slipping out of view of a farm to foreign places and then she speaks of all that she admired in her sister, beauty, seriousness, the ability to talk of political and vexing subjects. 'You made us see things differently. You – you lifted us up. You – you gave us something.' A woman in a brown suit walks out of Ireland again; she confronts with equanimity streets in Berlin and squares in Bucharest. Suddenly Mrs. McDermott realizes it is not her sister she is trying to talk to, to compose a song to, but her son Eugene. For years she has wanted to say something to Eugene but now he has ultimately eluded her. She has wanted to say that maybe she did something wrong but she does not have the words to say it. Words were never her forte; words fail her. So instead she settles for a prayer for the repose of her sister's soul over a glass dome at which a little boy in a blue coat had once peered in, eager for what was below, and she walks away.

On the train to Dublin she opens a prayer book to find the Mass card with her sister's face on it still intact.

In Dublin she stays with her daughter. Her daughter is going grey now. She no longer shares her suburban house with girl companions. Leaflets for societies of which she is on the committees lie about, societies for the betterment of the poor and those in dire social circumstances. The two women have tea in the evening. Earlier, Mrs. McDermott had taken a bus through Dublin in the midsummer light. She was pleased – as a child – by the neon in the sky, the colours of the light over the Liffey, the young, self-engrossed, passing men. Mrs. McDermott's daughter asks her now about Eugene, if he was coming home this summer. The reply is negative. There is silence and lack of comment. Why had he to go in the first place? Ireland could afford him a good job in the field of social work; soon he could have been climbing these heights of mountainside suburban houses. Mrs. McDermott says nothing. Mrs. McDermott's daughter rises and makes more tea. Afterwards they turn on the television to watch the late news and confront the colour image of Mrs. McDermott walking alone to prepare for the canonization of the first modern Irish saint.

[3]

They used to look up her bum, the nuns. Sabina Finnerty wakes up in Los Angeles, amazed that she is still alive after last night's sleeping pills, rises from the immaculate, expansive sheets, ignores the little poodle yelping lividly at her feet and confronts the long narrow mirror. At school when one of the doll-tiny, virginal latrines was soiled the nuns would line them up, pull up their skirts and inspect their bottoms to see who the culprit was. Now her body is scrawny and soured. Her nipples are overlarge and her pubic hair tired. But at least she's regained possession of her body. She poses like a forties model, one slender leg at a decorous angle, and lifts her hair in a bountiful mass above her head. Of late she's allowed the grey of her hair to show through, no longer hiding it with raven dye. The yelping of her dog becomes too much and she dresses, administers make-up, feeds the dog and then has her own breakfast which consists of coffee

150

and cereal. The December morning outside is blue and looks warm. Sabina welcomes it. Of late she's stopped taking male visitors. The last one brought a black rubber penis – like a seal – with one eye in it. God help us! Sabina now survives on Federal funds. After breakfast she buttons her strawberry coat to her neck and proceeds down the narrow stairs, bringing her dog for a walk. A neighbour listens, ear to a door. 'There goes the leprechaun queen. There goes the Connemara colleen . . .' Sabina takes the rebuffs with dignity. 'Good morning Miss Finnerty.' Mr. Hoberman greets her from his brightly lettered baker's booth. Sabina stops to purchase a newspaper. The small fresh print rushes at her. Szelenyi. Anders. Salamon. Yoshimasu. Foreign names float by. The cameras are rolling. Sabina sails on.

On a bench by the ocean, her dog tied to it, she opens her newspaper. A long funnelling funeral in Belfast greets her on the front page. For some reason she's been thinking of Ireland a lot recently, but not in a dastardly way. Her young cousin sent her an invitation to her forthcoming wedding. She refused it of course. Last time in Ireland Sabina's poodle piddled on a new sofa in some relative's house – a relative who hadn't long before been living in the bogs mind you! – and the piddle had a flush of mysterious pink in it. Sabina's been thinking of the main street of the town she came from, the bouquets the seasons once had made; green trees; in autumn the king of the fair paddling in the overgrown green of the fair Green, holding out his tinsel sceptre. She has been remembering the flushed gardens about the canal; the canal master's in particular – lupins, fox-gloves, airy asters. She's been remembering the gardens that spiralled from the main route into town, when she on a donkey spied them, the houses of the rich – doctors, solicitors – tiger-lilies and dwarf dahlias having orgies. It was the world, the raiment of her childhood. But subsequently that world had tried to destroy her. How she hated it. It was not the ignorance, the cruelty, the insults she hated most, but that attitude of theirs that it was no good trying, that all attempts at trying were bound to fail, that you were bound head and foot to the past, to atrophy, and there was nothing worth doing about it. They'd tried to pull her down with their stares. They'd tried to unloose every nerve in her body, in her intuitions, and maim them. They'd tried to take something from her; something she'd never have been able to get back. Oh yes, she's failed. But at least she tried; she had her moments against the silver screen and there was that moment in Iowa, among the cornfields, when she'd been at peace with history and with herself. More than anything they'd asked her to abandon hoping. She'd never, ever abandon hoping, never as long as she lived. She'd go on.

She becomes angry. She wants to cry. Alternately she wants to declare a truce with the town but she knows that can never be and anyway the town is miles away. Instead she rises with her dog and paper and walks on.

Buses traipse up and down the coast, stopping at irregular intervals. Later, although December, youths will inevitably wash in on the sunset, surfers. A passing woman throws a jealous glance at Sabina. Sabina is dining on carmine, scintillating, wet lobster with Montgomery Clift in an open air restaurant in Carmel-by-the-Sea. Montgomery is rising from expansive, newly laundered sheets, pulling a brief dressing-gown on him, after making love to her. It is the opening night of *The Heiress*. Tunnels of light search the night. Outside the cinema, although it is his night, Montgomery stops and sees her for the first time behind a barricade – an equal.

[4]

Being in a South London mental hospital in 1969 you met strange people; those who were convinced we were on the edge of the apocalypse and yet insisted on dressing in intricate Arab dressing-gowns; women who'd left their age-old grocery stores in Cracow for the West; the young permanently trapped on a flight of drugs. Denise came to see me. She dressed in black. She made a vocation of coming to see me and then became vague and stopped coming.

[5]

Being in the mental hospital, I took the opportunity to read books on Irish history. In my red jacket I carried piles of the books past paedophiles from Clapham in their dressing-gowns, their mouths agog. My mother came, in black; stood silently in the sloping mental hospital garden against the London sunsets looking much as she might against Galway sunsets smashing through stone-walls. It was she who kept me with a constant supply of these suspect items. I wanted to find out once and for all about things that preyed upon my mind; everyone was finding out. So I made Alan's journey through Irish history.

As a little boy in school his mind had gone back to the days before Spenser; he saw and approved of Munster as it had looked then. In the seventeenth century he was a poet among the mud, lamenting the family who had once employed him, disappeared to Europe. The eighteenth century was livelier. He was a red-haired poet who worked his way as a sailor to the West Indies. He travelled; London, Chester, but he returned to his native Ireland to die. In the early nineteenth century, Alan was a hedge school-master and in the latter part of the century he found himself a young Catholic seminarian. In the twentieth century he metamorphosed into what he would become, a curly headed, black haired young school-teacher with an obsession with history and a novel, taking its theme from history, in a drawer.

'A currach converges on a place of pilgrimage in medieval Ireland. A gull, which seems to have been following them all the way from Galway, dips over the boat. The journey from Galway has taken days and days. A little boy sinks deep into the boat. Cattle had crossed their paths, varying shades and shapes of cattle. Nearing Tyrconnel the women had stood back in cowskins, holding their children, looking at them, these starved and wild haired women, as if it was them, Lorcan and his mother and their fellow passengers, who had usurped the lands of Tyrconnel. One particularly wild haired woman, holding a child, was heard to whisper a curse or a prayer. The currach leaps now over the grey, choppy waves; distant low-lying mountains are covered by grey. "The devil lives in those mountains," a boatman mutters, "O'Donnell once had the devil by the tail." Now the devil rules Tyrconnel. As evidence of this a gruff bishop stands to in the bow of another currach leaving the shore. In the front of yet another stands a rotund woman, a white mantle around her head, her body wrapped in unexpected claret, an eagerness for penance on her face. They file out as the currach pulls up on the rocky shore. Women, who look as if they'd like to eat children, greet them, their ethereal bodies in black, their eyes blackened. A man plays pipes that look as if they have gangrene; another man, one legged, on the rocks has an intimate conversation with Saint Malachy as if with an old friend. Lorcan holds his mother's hand. There's stale bread in that hand and they catch it together, ensnaring it as if it were their last supper. As the blackness of night falls and the lamentations, the prayers, the exhortations of women grow louder, one becomes aware by the shrieking of those foolish enough to enter – some people come here on

153

bets – of the presence of the gate, the trap door, the corridor of hell. Lorcan's mother prays before an open-air grotto, a lizard-like, white, spinsterish Saint Brigid rebuffing her prayers. Lorcan wanders off. A litany is being said here. A story is being told there. Someone is selling turf from a sacred bog. A small crowd has gathered around a man who has survived hell; only splurges of *uisce bagh* from a bucket will make him recount his ordeal. A woman who looks about one hundred surveys him. He tells of what he has seen: nuns naked except for their veils, cherishing pet toads over a burning quagmire; monks, errant in this life, hopping like grasshoppers over the smashed and sharpened jewels of monstrances; portly bishops stalking with croziers topped by panther skulls. A little black-haired boy listens, his blue eyes gazing at a small fat man in a white tunic whinging between slurps of alcohol, the little boy's lips tremulous, big, red, foreign to this country. A man, obviously some kind of aristocrat, is so aghast by the descriptions that he takes to a secret load of Spanish wine wrapped in sackcloth his servants have been carrying.'

It was not a medieval Irish hell Alan Mulvanney went through, but a hell of Irish small town streets, of decorous shop façades. Right from an early age he was singled out, his black wavy hair, pale skin, red lips, against an Irish street. He was neither girl nor boy. His brothers tried to annihilate him; his mother turned away from him; teachers scorned him. There was the day when, in his little blue coat, his pants were removed under a reservoir by the Shannon and he was left to walk home without his trousers. 'Prissy prick,' the boys who did it called him. So Alan took refuge in the imagination – through the imagination he fought the effects of an Irish small town street – and history grew in the imagination. 'I suppose from an early age I was wounded so I adopted the ultimate wound – history. But that too had its consequences.'

On a second floor corridor of a gaunt, red brick Victorian building I caught up with a part of Alan I hadn't known before; skeletal old men in their dressing-gowns watched as I crossed an edge into a summer's day. In my red jacket I was one moment among the harvest fields, the next in a dark corridor. There was a thin border between my mind and the mind of someone else.

It was a day in late summer 1933. Young men gathered to leave on a Roscommon farm. A black surgical cab drew up. A woman emerged from the farm-house armed with a flask of holy water from Saint Patrick's Purgatory, County Donegal, proceeded to flail the holy water on everyone, including the cabman. One young man wore an ostentatious red rose over the jacket pocket of his pin-striped suit –

154

'The last rose of summer'. Other young men were more sedate. But all of them were returning to build Britannia's highways, to break their necks constructing the king's roads. The young man with the rose looked to the fields. The harvest was complete, the fields were stacked, low gold scintillating.

Far from the spectacle of farewells, a young man skirted the fields. All day something had been troubling him but he wasn't sure what. This summer on the farm had been different from other summers he'd spent on the farm. Athlone had caught up with him. People had not treated him as kindly as before. But now, as he wandered, stories he'd heard here in childhood jumbled in his mind, stories of Cromwell and Sarsfield; the mustard sky over the massacre at New Ross, the bloody red in the Shannon during a foray by Patrick Sarsfield – the colours of the stations of the cross in small rural Irish churches. But despite the sunshine a darkness was accumulating in him now like the darkness in an Irish church as scarfed women muttered and gesticulated the stations of the cross.

Soon he'd be back in Athlone. The boys would start bullying him again. But somehow negativity seemed less negative; negativity made his limbs sprightlier, his legs longer, fleeter, it blew his black gypsy hair outwards. In this knowledge, he took long confident strides now.

The boys on the farm had been less deferential to him this year. They'd turned away from him really, abandoned him. Only a youth was kind to him, a red-haired farm labourer who stooped a lot, didn't say much, meditated over his spade, lived with his father – his mother was in a mental hospital – and liked wearing a nice dark suit and a flashing scarlet tie.

The other young men laughed at him; they sneered at him. He was the farm idiot, the farm clown though he verbalized few idiocies.

One day he approached Alan, spoke to him. Alan was sitting on a fairy fort, a little mound of crumbled stone.

'I'd be careful if I were you.'

'Why?'

'Ah, it's haunted.'

'Haunted?' Alan looked up.

'The fairies.'

'I don't believe in fairies.' Alan was growing up.

'There are fairies you believe in and fairies you don't believe in. Around here the fairies are a wild lot. Roscommon fairies have a reputation you know.'

With that the red-haired lad went on with his digging.

Later in the summer Alan heard how he'd gone to a dance the other

155

boys on the farm attended. There was a slow beginning to the dance, boys on one side, girls on the other. Two fifty-year-old women danced to 'Slievenamban', one woman's rosary slipping out of her pocket during the waltz. The red-haired boy sat alone. The lads back from England were out for 'cunt', as they would say themselves; the summer hills reeked of pubic hair. It smelt of women in heat to them. They wanted 'a bit of cunt' they told one another, so they gathered awkwardly. Men and women were slow to dance with one another and when they did the girls seemed uniformly concerned about virtue that night – as if they'd planned it in uniformity. They whispered in the lads' ears about confraternities and solidarities. They abandoned the bald space of the centre of the floor as if they were all going to fly off to Egypt to be missionaries. The youths' eyes lingered on their behinds. The red-haired boy reclined near the women – sufficiently away from them not to be offensive – at the end of the hall near the back door. He seemed impervious to music, just sitting there. As women filtered away, choking with little shared feminine witticisms, strong in their imperial lack of concessions to men, the red-haired lad suddenly became noticeable. The amadán. Only forty-year-old virgins were left. They took him, the other farm lads, in the car of a friend – a general store owner's son from Roscommon town – and dumped him that night in a bog hole. He had to wander home alone in the dawn light, the bog cotton whispering with light and elfin and spying pink over the black bog hills.

After that his gait on the farm was more fumbling, more awkward; lost. There was a strange thing about this lad. He let his red hair grow long. But it was becoming.

The young man in the fields suddenly started running. He ran – remembering the red-haired boy – for dear life. He ran, in transit across the sun. The sun was silvery. It was the sun of Irish legend. Alan wrestled like Cúchulainn with the sun. An oak tree against the sun beaconed to his prowess. A white mare whinnied in his direction. A goose politely saluted him beside a pool under a sty which Alan flew across with ease.

Elsewhere on the farm the young men were finally getting into the car, all farewells said. A woman was exhorting the blessing of every saint and would-be saint. A puckish, red-faced young man grinned inanely, one hand on the door of the black shining car. An old man stood back, a bowler hat held in front of him with his two hands.

As Alan nears a barn his steps slow. There's something in there. The barn rears. It opens its gates.

In the mental hospital I could smell the hay, the sun in occasional

156

glints on hay, the more frequent darkness. The mental hospital building was one that demanded its due of ghosts; I had brought the ghost of a harvest day.

Each step on the ladder is an eternity. The contumelies reach a berserk pitch. His brothers – 'You woman.' His mother – 'Time to grow up, Alan, time to grow up.' His teacher – 'Cissy Mulvanney.' Sunlight suddenly hits the head of a black-haired boy who gasps as he confronts a red-headed boy, hanging from a beam in the loft, his blue eyes open and his tongue out in death.

'Priests in red and white wobble in alligator formation over scattered roses of Sharon in Galway city. It is Corpus Christi 1643. The churches have been reopened, Saint Mary's, Saint Nicholas', the Franciscan Friary. All Galway celebrates. The lord mayor, Sir Valentine Blake, preens by in a shining scarlet, no longer the worn blue one he was forced to wear in more adverse circumstances. Only a little girl, in the watching crowd, notices – and points to – the darned holes in his hose. Deep in the throat of one of the priests the 'Te Deum' gurgles and rises. Soon it is carried by all of the priests. Fishermen stop on the sea. Mules falter on the shore. The English have gone. Under a huge cross especially erected on the High Middle Street is piled lavender from the garden of Saint Brigid's House of the Lepers, brought here by lunatics in the charge of a Carmelite nun, one, momentarily doleful looking at present, on a leash in the nun's hand.'

My mother meets Alan at a harvest marquee. She'd never met a young man like him before. Something of the occasion, the blue dresses, the orange and blue lights around the Shannon remind her of the Corpus Christi procession in her home town the previous June. But as she walks with him by the Shannon, in spite of herself, she cannot help but let her thoughts fly. What would it be like to be in bed with him? What is his penis like? Is it white and nimble like his fingers which touched her waist so gracefully in a waltz?

'Two young people take leave of a castle in Connemara. Although it is summer the castle looks wintry against the sea, abandoned now. A girl, red hair ruffling her russet eyebrows, remembers the volcanic fires of childhood, wooden dolls from Italy, black with emerald eyes, priests scurrying over wet piers, just arrived from Europe, books under their arms, bursting with contents or yearning to be filled. The blond hair of two boys standing alongside the couple on the horse blows into one another.'

'Alan I'd like to take your photograph against the yellow cabbage seed by the Shannon next summer. You'd look great in your white shirt against the yellow cabbage seed by the Shannon. That's the way

157

the world will see you. I'll borrow my brother's camera, look down into it until you swim in it and click.'

'Swans fall onto a beach in Connemara; a strange confetti. Two young people stand over and look down at the gaping fan of blood on the extended neck of one of the swans.'

In a London mental hospital I got out of bed. I knew why Alan could not make love to my mother. It had been a kind of curse. As my mother had lain over Alan he could still see the blue eyes, red hair of a young man who'd committed suicide in County Roscommon in 1933 because he'd always been belittled. That had been Alan's story too. He'd always been belittled. That young man in County Roscommon had metamorphosed many times, into Red Hugh O'Donnell – a companion of a summer – into a novel, but he'd persisted because he'd been a fact in Alan's life, a death sentence. Right from an early age Alan realized he'd come from a tribe which did not tolerate a certain kind of young man, which dangled him, like a kitten, over the Shannon, then dropped him in.

A young man's face held sway now. It was not the face of the young man who'd committed suicide in County Roscommon in 1933 or that of Red Hugh O'Donnell, but a mixture of these people's faces and more – partly that of a young man in an Irish pub in Leeds in the 1950s and that of my friend Eugene McDermott. It was a fictitious face and yet it seemed independent of any one imagination, a unit, a life in itself. All this time, all these years it had been growing, it had been coming together, piece by piece – in a café on a small town Irish street, on Tottenham Court Road – it had been under the surface of things – a sheath of freckles – it had been in the storm clouds of red, in the whites of a boy's eyes, it had been in a boy's white, blue rimmed, sleeveless jersey, it had been in the mosaic of oranges and chestnuts and reds in a boy's thick hair. It was a face which took form out of the centuries, remembering a history which had tried to destroy it and more recently a country which had tried to destroy it. A young man in London remembering a hillside farm, squalling with gulls and rain, in Kerry. A young man in London remembering a rainbow on a Kerry bay. It was part of me and yet different. But in finally taking on completion, in standing outside me, I found there was an infirmity about the young man, about the vicissitudes, the shades of his hair, the stillness of his freckles. He existed in another realm. When I went to speak to him, to address my loneliness to him I found he could not hear. His presence was sufficiently comforting though. He was the brother I'd always wanted, the reassurance of a friend I'd always wanted. He was someone, had I known him earlier, I could have spent nights in a café on a small town street or nights on Tottenham Court with. But as it was I had to make do with these moments. I tried to hold on to them. I tried to draw them out.

The pipes ran along the walls with more urgency. The young man was as far as I could go with the quest of a part of me. He was the red-haired youth in the fawn anorak, a record under his arm, I'd once followed at night down Tottenham Court, past the sex shops, past the record shops, because he'd reminded me of the part of me conceived between Eileen Carmody and Alan Mulvanney.

As the face lingered snow began to fall behind it as in a blast in a glass ball; in this snow young men were rescued from castles, battles fought on frozen waters, cows seized in forays – the collective images of Irish history. But the young man was impervious to these images. He had conquered history, nationality, he had gone beyond these things. He appeared as he might have had these things not existed. His red hair burned in waves against the snow, his blue eyes brimmed with mirth, freckles ran in gentle consternation over his face, nearly choking him at the gulf of his white collars and blue denim jacket. His lips seemed about to make a statement. But he said nothing. There was no history, no nationality, no memory. The young man had crossed the limits into safety and into his posterity.

As my mother had lain over Alan he could still see the blue eyes, red hair of the young man who'd committed suicide in County Roscommon in 1933, a death sentence. They had long ago declared Alan's uselessness, his impotence. There was no use struggling against ancient cruelties.

Outside the long, narrow mental hospital window I could see Alan, his curly black hair, his long coat, his dreams of history, his sexual dreams. There was that novel in his eyes. It seemed appropriate Alan should have locked it in a drawer, for he came from a silent convocation of a world; they clamoured now, the people of that world, they demanded expression – girls on bicycles by late summer canals dotted with reeds, young couples waltzing across the shining ballrooms of the thirties. It had fallen upon Alan to find expression for this world and he'd done it through an image of history. Alan's black hair dipped back now into a time when woodcocks and partridges allegedly hopped in abundance in Munster, when laburnum ran riot from the gardens of aristocrats, when furze was a drunken gold. In his long coat a century later, he'd stood on a beach in Kerry and watched a family of aristocrats, who'd possessed a garden of laburnum and red hawthorn, push a boat off the beach at night, taking off to Europe. Alan should have gone with them. As a poet he'd lamented their passing, himself sitting among the mud and ruins of their former proud abode. The eighteenth century found him as a sprightlier, red-haired Kerry poet, working his way in a ship to the West Indies. He returned however to die in his native Kerry, among the sunken vases. In the early nineteenth century, beneath the red hawthorn that still blossomed, in profuse rags, Alan was a young hedge school-master, teaching Virgil and the great Socrates to dirty faced and bare footed waifs. The latter part of that century surprised him in a soutane. He was a young cleric in the newly opened Catholic seminary in Maynooth. In the twentieth century Alan was a young, curly haired, national school teacher, in Athlone, who'd written a novel and who imparted lessons about a time when woodcocks and partridges allegedly hopped in abundance in Munster. All that time Alan went on, despite the fact he knew they were after him. He was surrounded by an insidious encouragement towards death. They had long ago put a gun in his hand and told him to do away with himself. They did not want him. He ruffled them; their memory. My mother, a little girl at school, helped him resist. But eventually it became too much. He began to run. In his long coat he fled through the scintillating yellow cabbage seed by the Shannon. He stumbled across the tennis court, hiding in the vanilla shelter, watching the rain through the window for hours. Long limbed boys in blue and white striped jerseys beat a ball with hurleys on a radiant field as he slinked down a country lane, trying to race the stone walls. In the Genoa café he clutched a coffee. He ran down the main street, passing the cinema outside which Red Hugh O'Donnell was last seen at the end of the summer of 1939 – next to a cinema poster and a poster congratulating the recent fascist victory in Spain. They were on his heels. He eluded them down the labyrinth of alleyways beside the Shannon. The shop fronts, the street façades had become more modern, newer when he surfaced again on the main street. He could hear the crunch of their boots. In a flash he could see the blue eyes, red hair of the young man who'd committed suicide in County Roscommon in 1933, a young man resuscitated imaginatively many times. This time the young man had become Alan. They were all around him. I could see Alan, his black curly hair, his long coat, lying among the grass. There was a bullet hole in his head. They had murdered Alan Mulvanney.

'But I say unto you, That every idle word that men shall speak they shall give account thereof in the day of judgement. For by thy words thou shalt be saved and by thy words thou shalt be condemned.' My father died when I was in the mental hospital. I was allowed out for the funeral at which my mother stood over the grave in Old Brompton Cemetery as if she was going to throw herself in. Ladies, down from Northumberland, sponged their whiskers in cream cakes in the White City flat after the funeral, vociferously remarking on the excellence of the cream cakes, on the beauty of Old Brompton Cemetery. In my red unmourning jacket I noticed inscribed on the wall of the block of flats opposite 'Paul I miss you still.'

Back in the mental hospital I chanced to open the main door to a woman selling heather. 'White heather for luck.' The palm of her outstretched hand was blanched and bruised-looking.

Ghosts disappeared into the night; they vacated the spaces between walls, they gurgled down gutters. White corridor gave way to white corridor, to the pipes running along the walls. I groped along. There was a space to be filled now.

I began keeping a dairy which might have been the beginning of this; sheafs of white, screaming, ruffled paper in the bin, poetry books, alcohol, clothes packed and ready to go, army noises, a hush – in the night outside – that could still carry either life or death.

2 December 1969. Father dead. Mother in widow's weeds. She's always been in them anyway. Two countries to choose from. Which one will it be?

6 December 1969. Went to the National Gallery today. With a nurse called Mathilda. She led us, mainly teenagers clutching *Teen-Love*, as if we were a bunch of mongoloids. One girl said Monet's *Waterlilies* were the colour of Donavan Leitch's face.

14 December 1969. Met a nice girl today. Margaret Lucy. She insists on both names. She was called after a missionary aunt who walked by mistake into the Ganges in India and drowned. Margaret Lucy is here because she loves Jesus too much. She wears a heavy red check shirt, has long blonde hair with an angelic fringe, the angelic tips of her nipples showing through her shirt. She stopped me in the corridor and asked me if I prayed to Jesus. I said no but I could always start.

I refused to leave the premises of the mental hospital that Christmas. In my red jacket, with other demented youngsters, I left multi-coloured crackers in tatters and danced to rock music. My mother came to see me. In black. She'd been shopping in jumble sales for black. I ignored her. In the New Year I left the mental hospital. I did not go home. I went to live with the Jesus people in Bayswater.

Jesus was a child.
Jesus was a child.
But his blue eyes they spoiled
And his tunic they soiled.
They battered his brains
Into a thousand drains.
And they tore out his heart
And dumped it in a cart.
And they left him in a lump
In a rubbish dump.
But the child lives.
The child gives.
The love they could not kill.
The eyes they could not still.

I was soon found to have a talent for song-writing and posted, with a guitar, at Marble Arch to entertain visiting American ladies. At nights, Margaret Lucy and I made love to the sound of celestial choirs, rocking a fragile bed, but one night the celestial choirs became diabolical choirs – cinders sprang with tunes – that city returned: orange lights, miles of prostrate sacks voluminous with anonymous contents – to the sound of the infernal hit parade I leapt out of bed and ran naked down Bayswater into the arms of a hefty young policeman at Marble Arch. This time I was not sent to a mental hospital. In a black shining police car I was brought home.

A young man in a red jacket walks into a house on Holland Park; the carpets are rolled up, the ghosts of nights of sex and drugs and rock and roll languidly bathe in the sunny air – bluebottle shapes of dust. Another young man walks out and crosses Holland Park, Indian signals of smoke over the leaves alongside the paths, an old man, his head dipped under a cap, whistling a tune the young man has never heard before.

I began hating her, my mother, I began hating her for what she'd done to me, what she'd given to me, a consciousness. I wanted to hit her, I wanted to slap her face.

The young man in the house lies on the floor and covers his face in his red jacket. He does not want to see the world anymore.

I cut my hair, I nearly cut it off. I started working on building sites, any building site but one populated with Irish people. They were difficult to find, but it was possible. I became a nomad on building sites. In a mustard check shirt donated to me by Margaret Lucy, I indifferently dispensed darts into the air in pubs. I slimed my mouth with beer over pint glasses. With working-class companions, standing, I challenged television images of Northern Ireland. I'd lost nearly every nerve of an Irish accent. I'd regained, or thought I'd regained, what I thought I'd always been looking for, my working-class roots.

The young man on the floor lets out a scream. Even the mice, used to all kinds of debauchery, are terrified, stopping in their tracks by a mousehole, paws in the air, then scampering off to the nether corners of the house.

Black women with heavy black glasses on their noses trembled at bus-stops as I strode determinedly down the street, my eyes two little blue points running ahead. I'd all but forgotten. Only the random folk song of a busker reminded me, the busker's long blond hair falling out in increasingly more rapid stripes from his onion head.

[7]

The king has been a poor prisoner
A prisoner long in Spain.
And Willie of the Winsbury
Has lain long with his daughter at home

It was morning. The sky was blue. My father led me along. One boat upturned on the beach – blue like the sky – was called *Elizabeth* and a woman, seated on a chair on the beach with other women seated on chairs, who endearingly referred to the new queen as Beth, invoked a quick response from a sheepdog of the same name. Although it was summer, smoke was stranded in ermine wisps over the chimneys of the red village which lost its way halfway along. In the distance cloud rummaged on expanses of beach under low-lying mountains. My father had known some of these people, the women seated on chairs, old men animatedly mending their nets, since childhood. On another blue morning Ranters, Diggers, Anabaptists – whatever – had arrived in this village and, on a patch of beach, just below the village, which made do for the village square, got a pet bear

163

– a red scarf around his neck – to do a jig to melodion music and afterwards – if word of mouth was to be believed – ranted out one of their grating, anarchistic songs, all the time a little, blond, spiky-haired boy clashing a brass triangle. Now it was mainly left to the Methodist band to blow its bugles, for the most part from behind closed walls. As we walked along I knew my father was thinking about my mother. His face was gloomy. 'I'll not go up there,' she'd declared in Newcastle, 'They treat me like a battered golliwog up there.' I was in love with my mother's black hair. I'd never have hair like it. In her white sleeveless dress in front of a mirror she had whispered to me that if I was older she'd leave my father and marry me for I was a plucky lad. Then she'd turned to the mirror again and begun singing, 'The Boys from the County Armagh' at it. Suddenly on the beach, my father and I picked up the sound of a song at the same moment. On investigation, outside a pub, a little way up from the beach, we found a fat faced, red skinned, ginger moustached man belting out a song to an appreciative audience. Years later I recognised the tune. The song was about a king whose daughter sleeps with someone not of noble birth. The king decrees the death of the culprit until he is confronted by him and is so taken by the young man's beauty that he attests that he too would have slept with the young man had he been a woman. But for the moment what I was mostly aware of, apart from the tune, was a young blond man listening to the song, his hair standing up, askew, against the sun.

[8]

I started returning to Northumberland. The green of Northumberland I found lulling, the savage bonnets on distant, slim, aquamarine waves. I stayed with female relatives encountered at my father's funeral. The contents of cupboards were rummaged on my behalf; lemon dogs with panting strawberry tongues were clues to a former self, photographs of little boys in blue and white striped T-shirts, hands behind their backs, standing against the sea, were affirmation. I peered into the eyes of young soldiers serving in India in the early part of the century. The dark hair of young soldiers was turned blond by the sun. Another fantasy was growing. Chivalrously,

I escorted girls home from dances along by the waves; little upshoots of Methodist halls seethed with hymns on Sunday mornings. The high notes of hymns transported me. I was a little boy in a blue and white striped T-shirt being walked along a beach by his father.

Just to show her, just to punish her further, I brought my mother there, but she surprised us all, New Year's Eve 1971, in a Northumberland kitchen among the relatives and the cupboards, sitting, in a black dress, hair in a shining nest on her forehead, singing, as if in a drawing-room in County Galway abounding in photographs of male, white-shirted first holy communicants, and in plastic flowers, 'The Wild Colonial Boy'.

'There was a wild colonial boy. Jack Duggan was his name.
He was born and raised in Ireland, in a place called Castlemaine.
He was his father's only son, his mother's pride and joy.
And dearly did his parents love the wild colonial boy.'

I walked into the night. There was a moon that night. The shadow of a hill on a beach created a border between the years. I walked over that border into a photograph of a young soldier serving in India in the early part of the century. There was no turning back now. I was my father's son.

My mother's first reaction when I told her I was going to join the British army was to let out a howl of laughter; had she produced a human being or a hare? But when she saw me returning from the South of England to the White City flat in army uniform she turned away. I had joined the Cromwellians.

[9]

Eileen Carmody did not see her son for a few years. She heard from him often enough. He was in Germany. She imagined him, sitting alone in a dark pub, the red neon of the juke-box slashing the dark like a lighthouse, Jeremy sitting at the counter, one hand on a small glass of beer, a medley of pop music from all eras, all countries, in his ears. She followed him down back streets of German towns, a relentless and a harridan question in his eyes. How had he ended up in the army in the first place? How indeed? Eileen had often pondered that

165

question. She was acquainted with the notion that a person could have two personalities, but never could she have expected anyone to change as much as Jeremy had. There had been signs. It was as if she'd often seen people she'd known in his face. What strange flowers, what poppies had grown in the membranes of his brain? Perhaps she should have reached to him when worlds, when universes seemed to have been shifting under his feet. Maybe she'd failed to make the gestures towards him a mother should have made. Whether she had or not, to all intents and purposes Jeremy would have been the opposite to that easy boy in the red jacket were it not for the questions in his eyes which united him with that boy and many other soldiers, questions about why he was in the army, to what extent armies were instruments and manufacturers of aggression behind their front of defenders, what was his own degree of complicity in this silent process? She stood above him as he looked into canals from small, cobbled bridges. Would he or would he not throw himself in? 'May God and his divine Mother protect him.' One night he eluded her, slipping into a pub with a girl, a long, fawn coat, anxiously belted, on him, either replacing or covering his army uniform.

The purple and red neon of chemist shop windows in White City drove accusingly against Eileen on black nights. Yes, she was guilty. She had deposited the bomb under the bus, she had blown the youngsters in Birmingham to smithereens. Bingo ladies stole sneaky glances at her over games of cards in the flat. She did not declare her son in the British army. In a way she enjoyed the guilt of centuries being foisted upon her like the mop on her head. The bingo ladies suddenly left her life, not after an I.R.A. bombing, but, Eileen supposed, after some collective anti-Irish whim. She was not to be trusted. Eileen was left to walk the nights alone then. She watched television a lot, speaking to the grinning apes of compères, often snoozing off in front of their flapping dickie bows, dreams coming to her of white horses traipsing through Irish bogs in the 1640s bearing messages of peace. In a zone of black and white television screens Eileen had technicolored dreams.

The letters from her son tailed off for a while; resumed. He told her about his friends. Johnny was from Liverpool. Of Irish Catholic background. One of a family of fourteen. Dropped on his knees each night before going to bed in the army sleeping quarters to say his prayers as his mother had dictated he should do. Carl was from Edinburgh. An Orangeman. Hated Catholics. Jeremy did not reveal his Irish background to him. Jonah was so called because he'd slept with the biggest prostitute in the local village, but the nickname soon slipped off because he was as big as a whale himself. Simon played the violin. Just showed you not everyone in the army was an eegit. He was transferred to Northern Ireland. He was the first person directly or indirectly to cross Eileen's path to be killed in Northern Ireland, blown to a million, quivering, violin sonata pieces. Shortly after that Jeremy wrote to say he'd been promoted to sergeant. He must have been doing well for himself. She did not write to congratulate him. His new status raised the fundamental question as to how the army had been fooled by him in the first place. He'd probably presented such an unerring face, as only he could do, that he was mistaken for someone sane. Or maybe most people in the army were mad. Trying to work out this conundrum Eileen got the news that her son was to be married.

[10]

Saturday, 22 October 1976. Relatives crowd into a photograph after a wedding in Marylebone Registry Office, London, mainly ladies in turkey purples and scintillating vermilions, handbags hanging from their hands like dead hares. The bride is young, wears a white suit, has nice even legs, the right one inclined to her new husband who is in military uniform. He is austere and quite military looking. Only a woman stands out, in white, as if she too had bridal illusions, to the extreme right of the photograph, her eyes disdaining the mood of the photograph. It is a sunny day. Leaves twirl in the air, orange, red, an economy of leaves.

Afterwards there was a reception in a small hotel. Kaleidoscopic lights swooped on the backsides of the ladies, in suits and dresses resurrected from wardrobes near the sea and spruced for the day, who'd formed a train, their hands on one another's bottoms, and were making an uncertain voyage around the hall, the DJ addressing backsides he favoured.

The bride was from Huddersfield. Her people had come in from the moors where they'd lived between the hills, their faces dark as shoe polish and empty as saucers in a workhouse, without saying much to others or to one another. In the town they'd articulated themselves in different ways. Some had chosen the red wastes of blocks of council flats among the wastes of rubbish dumps and

167

annihilated earth. Others had prospered. One of them owned a string of garages in Huddersfield, another a night club in that town. The latter's pride in life was his racehorse called Meadowsweet who constantly plied the earth with her feet. He was said to have murdered a cousin when both were eighteen, sticking a knife in his heart among the heather, but Suez had come up and he'd never been brought to law, packing his bags and heading in the direction of Egypt instead. It was he who'd financed tonight's proceedings, Marion's, the bride's, parents being among the poorest of the relatives. He sat now, feeding on cigars, his pot-belly supporting a pink shirt and a polka dotted tie, an Al Capone type moustache savouring the aromas of the cigars, his glassy eyes on the property he'd purchased, the sliver at the top of Marion's buttocks.

When she was a little girl Marion would swirl a hoolahoop around her hips near the sites of used tyres, continually supplied by her garage owning uncle, and chant a rhyme at the same time which made a plea she'd meet a prince one day. With this end in mind she threw on a coat and left Huddersfield, where she'd been a waitress in a fish and chip café, and worked her way, as a waitress, down through motorway cafés on the M1, ending up, with her high qualifications as a waitress, serving in a British Army canteen in Germany. While in Germany she met her prince, a young man whose accent was difficult to define, reminding her of American film stars in films pushed into television or shown in capsizing cinemas in the backstreets of Huddersfield.

Her prince stood now to the side and alone. His people were from Northumberland. They were poor people but, like her people, counted rich members among them. They had houses by the sea, photographs of young soldiers serving in India, Burma, Ceylon on these maritime windowsills, exotic shells, passed on endlessly between generations. Among the bush of Burma and the junks of China were sometimes little boys in blue and white striped T-shirts, hands behind their backs, standing against the sea. They were generous people to their relatives and had turned up in generous numbers for the celebration of Jeremy Hitchens tonight, ladies kicking up their purpled knees. But also here was Jeremy's Irish mother whom he'd vaguely mentioned. Marion and he had spoken little of backgrounds. They'd made love a lot among the crevices and the backstreets of the German language, their bodies, their limbs finding a language of their own. But that language seemed to have failed them tonight. Jeremy did not seem to notice that Marion was trying to catch his attention.

Marion was twenty-two, had long brown hair replenished and straightened by much combing. Naked, Jeremy had told her she had a body like sea-shells and she in turn had told him he had a body like a house.

Jeremy's face had become more handsome since he'd joined the army. He'd modelled his face on an army photograph. But the photograph was puckering now. He looked with anxiety to where his mother was sitting alone, either by design or because she was being ignored, sipping a campari and soda.

They'd met in a bar or had it been a café? The women had turned out to be men, dark hair on the backs of their hands, short fur coats on them, red lipstick, dark wigs, their hands swinging. The juke-box cooed. Marion's hair had been in a bun at the back which made her look older and a heavy fawn coat had weighed her down. She cowered in a corner. Snow had begun to fall on the canal outside when they left for a small hotel.

'Isn't it a luvely night Mrs. Miles? Your dress is smashing. Where did you get it? The cleavage, never saw anything like that on a duck! Isn't she strange, Jeremy's mother? Those eyes, they'll burn a hole in the wall yet.'

In the morning they'd crossed the snow of the town. There were few people around and the castle was like an avalanche of snow high above them. Marion's head had dipped and the snow of the square absorbed the sound of their footsteps.

'Doesn't she look a right old whore. I'd like to get it up her.'

They'd made love a lot. They found they liked making love. Marion's body had looked like a cistern as she lay back. The top of Jeremy's penis was nearly always big and pink and earnest. But in the mornings life seemed to have lapsed from Marion's body when German canals were grey outside.

'She's all alone poor soul. Should we say hello? Maybe not.'

For Marion making love was a pop lyric. But strange fantasies crept into Jeremy's mind, his body lurching over hers – a little boy in a blue and white striped T-shirt, a red-haired youth.

During the course of the night word slipped out of an Irish connection and that gave the DJ a cue to line up his Irish jokes. He worked for a local radio station in Yorkshire but that at least, he claimed, was better than working for the Irish radio station. People paused, looked at the inadvertent object of attention, then danced on, madder, with more flexing of their limbs than before.

Red balloons bounced delicately around the edges of the hall, bloodied plastic flowers bowed, scarlet lights leapt on the walls. Dust and carnage collapsed on a trench in Flanders again. Feet raced across the white sands of Normandy, rifles held outright, backs stooped. Knitting problems were solved as a shower of bombs fell in the city of Coventry some two hundred miles away. Children's heads rolled after a bomb blast in Aden. Ships preened down the Suez canal. Terrorists were shot in Northern Ireland. Fists shut high in the air, atrophied legs faltered in rising, bottoms singed bottoms.

Marion was forced to dance by a seventeen-year-old boy from Huddersfield, the whole of him, from the vapour of hair over his forehead, to his new suit, grinning.

It was she who'd suggested marriage. She'd been wearing that heavy coat, sitting in a café, Jeremy standing over her. Light from the grey sky outside had reflected on the ring from Woolworth's she was twiddling on her finger. Jeremy's face had remained as inscrutable as ever.

Jeremy had no choice but to cling to the overweight buttocks of a woman, her arms striped about his neck.

Afterwards they'd walked in a park and watched a little boy in a blue sailor's suit stoop over his yacht on a pond. Why not? It would be an occasion and it had been so long since there'd been an occasion in his life.

The DJ was now encouraging the delighted throng to dance to 'Who's your lady-love?' A black toothed old lady had cornered Marion who was standing on the side again and was proceeding to impart to her a catalogue of gynaecological advice.

It had been the packing Marion had enjoyed most. She'd always loved packing. She took down the pin-ups, delicately, one by one, from an otherwise bare wall in a room in an army barracks in Germany. Soon she'd have real possessions to pack.

Old men congratulated Jeremy, shaking his hand in their white, death-like ones. Middle-aged men and younger men guaranteed him he'd have a salacious sex life and many children. Young soldiers winked.

He should have told her, but it had been too late. Plans were already flying headlong.

There was a sudden blast of cigar smoke in Jeremy's face. 'So you're a bit of a Paddy.' The night club owner leered.

They'd taken a boat from Calais to Dover. They'd both stood on deck. Marion had been packed into that heavy fawn coat, a cumbersome thing, holding her stomach as if she were already pregnant. The sky had been white, white grafted onto it. Coloured lights had greeted them on a Dover promenade towards evening.

170

The DJ's right arm was in the air now like a victor's, his jacket off in an abortive striptease, a square inch of his black navel hair showing. Marion just wanted to be away from all this, in bed with Jeremy, close to the fecundity and aliveness of his genitals. But he did not seem to be aware of her now.

The first real sign of trouble had been a few nights before. There'd been a party for them in the army camp in Oxfordshire where they were now going to live. Army wives had sported lopsided paper hats. Bunting had bellied in the air. An officer had dressed as a woman, a handbag on his arm, and had sung a cabaret number, wriggling his slender hips. There'd been a stage where plays were sometimes produced and concerts performed. There was still a piece of scenery, a suggestion of a kind of Arcadian scene, white, oversize, agreeable waterlilies – yolky moons at their centres – at the bottom right-hand corner of a backdrop sitting up against black lake water and black down-sweeping mountains and black bogs. On this stage little lime-dressed, bespectacled boy scouts from the locality had choked their loyalty to the Queen, and one Saint Patrick's night bagpipes wailed. Perhaps inspired by the reverberations of these aftermaths – you could still smell the biscuits the little boy scouts had crunched in the wings – or conscious of the backdrop, Jeremy, who was very drunk, a pint glass in his hand, began telling a story. Everyone thought it was a children's story at first and began listening. The story book opened. There were illustrations of young couples on white horses wandering through black bogs and by black lakes covered in giant, white waterlilies. The trees were a different shade of green in this world, a darker shade but a more brilliant one. Fuschia burst, its tassels burnished. Little rain clouds puffed over mountains. A wandering couple on a white horse were temporarily lost from sight. But the child's images gave way to other images when these white horses and black lakes turned out to be specifically in the seventeenth century and more specifically, for most people, in Ireland. But by then it was too late. Jeremy began displaying his hands – they seemed very white – declaring that because they'd merely touched weapons, and it would have been the same if they'd merely touched them once, because weapons had been put in those hands they'd go on festering for ever. An army wife, a bottle of beer in her hand, looked about to blubber. The cabaret garmented officer was suddenly acutely suspicious. A blue paper hat took the opportunity of the silence to glide into a piddle of beer.

A huge, invisible, magical Union Jack enveloped the hall now, alighting on heads, shoulders, jaunting thighs. The Union Jack was

171

carried to the four corners of the earth, planted on top of the Himalayas, in a covert green spot in Asia, in Cyprus, in Ireland. An ancient man – ninety – nearly had a heart attack in the excitement of recalling an incident in the Boer War in which he shot at a zebra from behind a bush, mistaking him for an Afrikaaner.

Marion was finally going to Jeremy and Jeremy finally going to his mother. A parson from Huddersfield – a noted exorcist – looked at Jeremy and was sure he was mad. But before Marion could reach Jeremy and before Jeremy could reach his mother, a young man from Huddersfield, who worked part-time in a garage and part-time in a rock group, stepped forward, approached Mrs. Hitchens, who was still sitting alone, and asked her to dance. The request was conceded. The crowds fell back in the shadows as they took the floor and performed a tango, the young man's purple suit beginning at his pink socks – like a furnace. 'A curious street unfolds pictures.'

Marion was thinking of a night of love-making, a single, red, hermetic light from a brothel on the black canal surface outside.

I was thinking of a street in Ireland; a fifteen-year-old boy wrote a poem again, his red hair put together fragment upon fragment, against the lamplight, a bleach of freckles on his snub nose. Behind him was a photograph of his parents on their wedding day, 2 September 1939, his mother's smile punctured like a late summer rose, a piece of black, funereal taffeta on the breast of her sea-green suit, his father's face serene under hair, red like Eugene's. Also on the wall behind him was a calendar representing a local garage, this month's picture showing the fair Green. On this Green once, during the October horse fair, a little black-haired girl in a red tartan skirt, a blue and white tin caravan selling chips beside her, the grass of the Green thick at her feet, pointed to a creamy pie-bald Connemara pony and told Eugene that, according to her father, on such ponies her people were carried as kings through the pastures of Ireland once. A flight of primrose, chalk birds took place across the patterns of the wallpaper. The poem seemed to reach the page almost before the pen touched it. As he wrote, his red hair put together fragment upon fragment, footsteps clanked on the street outside. But neither boy, neither the one outside facing the otherwise empty street, nor the one inside, were aware of one another's presence. Gradually the footsteps died away. The poem was complete, the lamplight turned out and Mr. and Mrs. McDermott left to smile the smiles of a radiant autumn day in 1939 in the dark.

Gulls dipped over an army yard in Oxfordshire. Gulls lowered over fleshy crusts of white bread in the grey yard of a National school in Ireland. Mr. Hearne raged again. This time I knew what he raged about. Marion changed. She took to wearing tweed skirts, to patrolling the streets of Oxford in search of the right cheeses, the right coffees, to marooning herself in lamplight. A pool of red lamplight separated her husband and herself. We did not know one another. Marion started attending an evening class and wooden yachts appeared on the windowsill of our house overlooking an army quad in which genocidal officers howled at quaking recruits.

In December in Oxford, in my army uniform, I walked into a church; the winter solstice struggled through the eagle of Saint John, the Union Jack was suspended rigid, the trophies of war were up – Marion at my side I halted, knowing I'd trespassed as far as I could go with my Englishness.

That city returned – orange lights, prostrate sacks, the red-haired youth, a flicker of light now around the edges of his hair against flames or the scars of snow.

Years in the creation, you seemed so little when you finally arrived or you went so quickly. The oranges, the chestnuts, the reds, the saffrons even, connected me with a figure in history, with the fantasies of someone else in a summer in another time, with a part of myself. I created something and it became real and followed me and became my life.

I had declared war on a part of myself.

At Easter Marion and I took off for a holiday in London, a red light blinking on and off on the street outside throughout our first night in a Soho hotel, and when I woke in the morning there was an empty and disarrayed space in the bed beside me. Marion was not to be found. On my return to Oxfordshire a note awaited me. Marion had returned to her parents in Huddersfield.

I spent a few days in Majorca, in a blue Hawaiian shirt and white trousers, sitting, my dark glasses reflecting other people in blue Hawaiian shirts and white trousers, their activities, as well as the brimming blue of the sea and the engulfing effervescence of plants.

When I got back there was a message I'd been expecting for a long time. I packed my things and within a few weeks, with other soldiers, was crossing from Stranraer to Larne, the towers of Carrickfergus rising, the clouds of Ireland.

It is a morning in early summer in 1649. Two armies confront one another on the green hills of the western Midlands. On these hills once maybe Jesus trod. Both armies wear the same red coats. The one on the right, as we look, is determined. The other is an army of stragglers. They seem reluctant, pacifist even, on the point of battle. A faction of the New Model Army had broken away from the main body on its way to subdue Ireland and declared, in the spirit of the past decade, that England has no right to be in Ireland. It was a decade in which soldiers burst into churches with news of the new city. As the dissidents gathered earlier this morning on a hill, the flowering chestnut looking down approvingly at them, sharpening their scythes, pikes, swords, it seemed as if they could see that city rising in the plains below them, its towers, its backstreets. They were so familiar with those backstreets, especially in early morning when there was a market. They knew the fishwoman and the bakers by name. But they might not have had cause for such optimistic visions. In January the king had been executed, his outheld ring scintillating in the winter sunshine as he strode to his place of execution. But he was not the only one to go. Recently the Leveller leader Robert Lockier had been executed and buried amid rosemary dipped in blood. A community in Sussex, whose children had no one mother or father, were massacred by locals, the locals rising up against them, declaring them to be adulterers and infidels. But in spite of this, fiddle music started up from somewhere and two young men sprang up and did a jig with one another. As they did another young man grabbed flowers from the hillside, bluebells and buttercups and daisies and cowslips and lilies, raised them to the sun and addressed the sun. 'O Christ of the Resurrection preserve the rainbow in us. Preserve hope and truth and compassion and love in us. O Christ of the Resurrection preserve the sun in us.' He had frayed silk, forced march torn, red – pale red with oblongs of deeper red stencilled onto it – hankerchief tied around his neck. A little blond boy gaped in awe at all this from behind a bush.

His awe might well be justified now. Last night Malcolm Prendergast from Bristol and Terence Firth from Thanet in Kent spoke eloquently to one another over firelight about the problem of history; there were those who had to go against history Terence had stated, there were some who had to try to break the power of history. The price of going against history is paid now. The main body of the New Model Army, hesitant at first against the green and sacred hills as if waiting for the tableau to be gauged, iron over faces, muskets and pikes steadied, coats one clean scarlet flame, suddenly move in against their adversaries and with more force than they will show in Drogheda, Wexford, New Ross, cut them to pieces until young men are dying, limbless, wailing among the occasional bushes of wild white dog roses shadowed now by fleeting clouds.

There is silence that evening as women and black dogs wander among the dead and the New Model Army have departed, forging their way through the royal green of England, to Ireland.

[13]

I had a dream the other night. I was sitting in a café in my red jacket. The window was clouded over. The juke-box played. A young man came to the window. I could not make out his face but he had red hair. He was the brother I never had and always wanted. He was the friend I never had and was always searching for. He was trying to tell me something. I went out into the street after him but there was nothing there but orange lights, at first a few of them, then miles of them, and, as I stood there, tanks began to approach from both sides, at first slowly, then, towards the centre of the street, with the sound and velocity of war.

Epilogue

It is an afternoon in early December 1929. A picture of Blessed Oliver Plunkett dominates the classroom, his hair long, wavy, silvery, cavalier-like, his blue eyes pertinent, the wings of his collar white, his cassock maroon against the maroon and purple storm clouds of Ireland. He is the chief exhibit among the other exhibits, the Archbishop of Armagh hanged, drawn and quartered at Tyburn in 1681, situated above the wide blackboard. The other exhibits, brightly and profusely coloured, line the walls on both sides of the classroom. Their theme is history and the forlorn and tragic history of Ireland at that. Beginning on the left-hand side of the classroom, in the corner furthest from the blackboard, the side away from the Shannon, Brian Boru, High King of Ireland, shoos a last Viking from Ireland, the Viking clinging protectively to his bottom from behind, the undersides of his bottom, which we can divine, swathed in hair. A Viking ship disappears over the skyline, a stripe of dawn or sunset in the sky above, reflected in the Irish sea. This is to be one of the last notes of levity. In the exhibit immediately after, the fate of Ireland is handed over to the Normans by the treacherous Dermot McMurrough, a few dragon-like scarlet banners flurrying in the background. Now there is mainly just lamentation. Among the goriest is the sight of innocent Portuguese and Italians being personally hacked to death against the glorious Kerry sunset over the Skelligs rocks by the English deputy Grey at Dún an Óir 1580. Underneath a reminder. 'Fides Graie.' Grey had promised to let them be if they surrendered. There is an Irish triumph at the battle of the Yellow Ford and, just before the blackboard, the Spaniards dolefully leave Ireland after the Battle of Kinsale, in snail-like ships. The earls are about to go. Ireland is in the iron grip of the foreigner. At the blackboard we pause. Mary, the purity of her heart – she is pointing to her heart with her left hand, simultaneously looking into the air – are nibbled in white chalk on the blackboard. The teacher gives an accompanying homily on the purity of Mary. 'She was transported into heaven on a golden rug lined by scores of little pink roses.' Beginning on the other side of the classroom, at the corner nearest the blackboard, Eóghan Ruadh O'Neill, the Catholic general, dies, lying back on the green turf of Cavan, pulling back his military uniform to reveal his Dominican garb underneath and a spray of scapulars, the sky blood-red – as if all the blood of battlefields of the last few years had seeped into it – and watchful. This is to be a picture which influences Alan much; red being the colour of the jerseys he is to wear, red being the colour which most occupies his writing and his black, enlarged eyes. Ignoring chronology, presumably in order to restore some much needed gaiety, the scene after Eóghan Ruadh's death depicts Munro, the Puritan general, fleeing the Battle of Benburb in 1646, three years before Eóghan Ruadh's death, on foot, his wig having fallen off, his bald and silvery pate reflecting an imminent shower. Massacre follows massacre, a contagion of them around the time of 1798 when frail and vulnerable Irish insurgents rose against the English – New Ross, Vinegar Hill. Finally and more hopefully a broad and ghostly foreheaded Parnell receives an ivy leaf, on a platform above a mass meeting, from a girl in a shawl, the limestone and sturdy façade of the main street of a small Irish town in the background, sycamores in flower touching the limestone. As eyes in the classroom are looking in the direction Mary was transported, Alan busily writes a poem. He's never written a poem before but today he has the urge and he does it, head bowed. The poem miraculously appears in pale blue letters on a page of anaemic blue squares.

> Mr. Snowman.
> Mr. Snowman.
> You have pebble eyes.
> A big fat white tummy.
> You hold a broomstick.
> Someone stuck a leaf in your nose.
> A snail crawls on your hat.
> The snail has many colours.
> Do you long for colour Mr. Snowman?
> What do you ask for?
> You say nothing.
> Do you know it already?
> You're going to die Mr. Snowman.
> Do you look with your pebble eyes into your short life?
> Do you long for life Mr. Snowman?
> Is that the gift you ask for?
> But the sun climbs up.
> The day is blue and sunny.
> Very soon there's just your hat left and your pebble eyes.
> I pick them up and take them with me.

After class Alan gathers his coat from a shower of coats on a floor under a window in a darkened room and braces the air outside.

In his short blue coat, satchel thrown over his shoulder, poem in his pocket, he scampers along the main street, past the black cardigan and black skirts of Mrs. Devereux who is gazing into the opposite side of the street. Last year Mrs. Devereux journeyed to the United States in search of a daughter who years before had married a Protestant and gone to live there. It was relatively easy for Mrs. Devereux to travel to the United States because under the picture of a liner in front of her house was a store which sold, among other things, fresh tickets to the United States. She had four ports a day on the liner, four only she informed people on her return. With a long black veil which hung over her face from a hat, black like her dress, she could hardly see in New York and was nearly run over by automobiles several times – on Fifth Avenue, on East 47th Street where she was staying in a hotel owned by an Athlone man. Among evergreen plants, with no choice but to listen to melancholy music, she plaintively dipped into a dish called Clonmacnoise shrimps, Clonmacnoise being an ancient Irish monastic site by the Shannon, near Athlone, far from the sea where shrimps could be found, a place she'd gone on golden days at the height of the pug nosed queen's reign to dip her feet by buttercup banks and to air her rippling legs for the benefit of young gentlemen's eyes. But evidently such incongruities did not matter in New York. The shrimps Mrs. Devereux got looked like new born babies, slithers of purple and red on them. Skyscrapers swooned from side to side, in unison, as she stooped into a taxi which would take her to the station, the skyscrapers leering, also in unison, 'You'll be back. You'll be back,' ladies, their eyes made up, their arms linked around one another's shoulders, in a chorus in the Theatre Royal, Dublin, their petite and pale stockinged feet kicking up in effrontery against her. 'In the name of the Father full of virtue, in the name of the Son who suffered pain.' A refrain of Gaelic prayer jumbled into the many coloured syllables on a New York street on a sunny March afternoon. She was on her way. Buffalo and Indians, carrying their wigwams, trekked through the sky. Mrs. Devereux crossed by train to San Francisco from which her daughter had last written. Winter was lifting its mantle from America but she hardly noticed such was the weight of sorrow on her. Besides she had blistering chilblains. They were hidden deep in big black boots. An Indian man sitting opposite her asked her where she was from and when she said Athlone he thought it was something to do with loneliness. Indians, rugs on them, huddled on station platforms under the last flakes of snow. In

San Francisco her daughter was not to be found and Mrs. Devereux walked up and down the hills of the Golden City a few times to 'stretch her legs', the light from the Pacific and from the sky over the Pacific shimmering and unlike anything she'd ever seen. A mute Chinese man outside a casino smiled at the sight of her, this Irishwoman with her big black hat, veil pulled up from over her face, her dress pulled up a little way from her big black unsuitable boots. Light from the Pacific hit the Casino, golden because it was nearly evening. The two people looked at one another and could say nothing. She took the train back – this time in the direction of Boston to which apparently her daughter had moved. This time she noticed more of her journey, the vicissitudes, the fluctuations of America, the flowing birch trees, the blanched stripes of desert occupied only by sad slivers of Indians, the icy blue and sapphire rising mountains, the hidden densities of dark green with secret, white, opening flowers, the skeletal grey skies with skeletal cabins underneath, the more luxuriant plains, spring coming to a white dray horse and to yellow banqueting fields, the religious people – in carriages – in the hills, a child with a black hat on looking in at her, his white collar open, the cities again, the lakes, the citadels of cinemas against the evening, girls foxtrotting on the paraffin skylines, the forests, the leisurely plains, lakes again, then maybe the stalwart and morose Atlantic looking towards Ireland. Mrs. Devereux arrived in Boston just in time for the funeral of her daughter's first son who'd been drowned in a lake. It was credited that he was laid out on the green bank beside the lake under the Stars and Stripes, the angelic blond seven-year-old, in a scarlet shirt, his hand on his nearest and dearest toy, a wooden tram. How Mrs. Devereux had laid eyes on him no one knew but when she saw him, this grandson who would never wield a hurley in a blue and white striped jersey, she fell on her knees and cursed a God of the old world who had taken a child of the new because his mother had erred from the ways of the old. Now Mrs. Devereux gazes into the opposite side of the street, and gaggles of women in Athlone whisper that at the same time every day on the main street tears can be seen in those eyes in the limestone face.

Mr. Ahearne, the meanest man in Athlone, stoops in his white coat over grain in his grocery store as Alan flies by. Being mean in the meanest town in Ireland requires dedication. Mr. Ahearne is said to wander in his white coat deep into the bogs at dawn to bury sacks of money under gallow-like sprigs of bog cotton. On a shelf near the weighing scales is a photograph of two boys by the sea taken in Lahinch in 1895, two brown suited boys, Jacob and Benjamin, as in the Bible. Mr. Ahearne's two sons went to fight for the king in Flanders and died, so there was no propriety in their deaths, they did not die for Ireland. Mr. Ahearne got no laurels for their deaths. In the shop now among the bacon, the biscuits and the bulky monstrosities of cheese newly arrived from the creamery, two boys do what they do not do in the photograph; they run by, they sidle away from, they flee waves by the sea at evening, they are caught slant-wise against the sunset. Out there is Tir-na-n-Óg, the Land of Youth. It is the land of dead children, the land of fairy tales, of jars of honey on breakfast tables by the sea, of dickie bows, of first holy communions. Its red imminence incandesces in the shop now and connects Mr. Ahearne with stories Mrs. Ahearne, a Connemara woman, told these children at evening, in her deep west of Ireland accent, her hair dark, a moustache growing on her lips, a broad book open on her lap, a fountain of colour.

Someone much preoccupied with Tir-na-n-Óg is Mr. Stankard who is walking down the opposite side of the street from Alan. He is producing a pageant based on Cúchulainn's boyhood in the Temperance Hall for Christmas. The geography of Tir-na-n-Óg is of much interest to him but it is not of that he is thinking now but his love for the 21-year-old playing Cúchulainn as a boy. After rehearsal when the lights have been turned out, Mr. Stankard stays behind the backdrop showing castles and strange vegetation and black lakes and red trees and wonders what it would be like to kiss this boy, his fuschia lips, to herald his flannel trousers in his bony hands, to tell him how he was aware of him for years, on bicycles, by street corners, in hurling teams, how he followed him into changing rooms, how he watched him at parties after plays, under pictures of horse fairs on wide Greens, fiddles playing, the scene becoming a party in a big house in Ireland when a young man was about to fly with the wild geese. But it never happens and anyway the young man is leaving Ireland shortly after Christmas.

Alan bumps into a raggedy nun, Sister Divine who taught him at infants at convent school. She is eighty-nine. 'Good day Master Mulvanney.' Behind her fragile temples are memories of the famine around Athlone; a treasure-trove of skulls; gaping skulls enthroned on green hillocks everywhere; her family was one of the lucky ones, they went to America. She can remember the fourteen children in her family and her mother and father in the lounge of a posh hotel in Queenstown before leaving, God knows how they ended up there; barefooted and grimy children among the ferny plants in a hotel lounge, a kind lady bringing a tall cup of brimming coffee to her mother and hot milk to the children; the hotel had a pale and broad front. An ebony, peeling, shark-nosed ship took them to America. Its nose shone against the blue waves. Five children were lost on the journey. Bodies of babies were enwrapped in rugs bought in Athlone, and neatly tied and gently given to the sea. In Boston in a dense pier-side encampment for Irish immigrants her favourite brother Johnny died. He had survived the famine and the sea and then died of typhus, in a silk, embroidered shirt – discovered in a ditch once; did it belong to a landlord's son? – that had endured the Atlantic. He'd been the pluckiest and the most laughing of her ethereal faced brothers; it was with him she'd scurried to the cottage of Eibhlin Doherty to hear stories; it was with him she stormed fairy forts; it was with him she'd rested her head near straw and death on the journey over the Atlantic. Her mother sang him to sleep with a lullaby as Mass was said in Irish in a black encampment on a rainy twilit evening. It was said that it was his death which buttressed her resolve to return to Ireland; retreating into a black, Atlantic swept convent, becoming a nun; dedicating herself, life after, to teaching the infants class in the convent in Athlone. She had watched millionaires and reverend mothers pass through. England's famine had taken her brother but she felt no bitterness against England. She had built an aviary on the convent grounds, christened budgies and canaries with biblical and Gaelic names, sat in a grotto, walking-stick in hand, waiting to die and be rejoined with a brother who all these years, his wide open shirt and his smile broadening against the heavens, had been stamped in a brooch on her heart since his death of typhus in Boston in the 1840s.

'Hello, how are you? Good day. Nice day. Looks like rain. Snow surely. Is that the young one? Aren't you looking grand, you creature. Is that yourself Peader McGrath? Good afternoon. Good day. The doctor ordered that I try to regulate my bowel movements. There's a chill in the air, isn't there? Lovely day. Atrocious day. There were men in the field last night with lanterns – what were they up to? Excuse me. Good day. Is that Mr. Mulvanney's little nipper?'

Horses burrow deep into feeding bags; geese are trapped in the market place below the Protestant church; women look longingly at milkchurns in windows; little girls peer around the corners of black skirts; yellow chicks batter the walls of brown boxes; exotic carpets are laid out and contemplated by gruff ladies in little black puffs of hats, black puffs of bags in their hands; ancient clocks tick; in one window is a crib which indicates that Christmas is approaching, the magi delicately spy through a door on the Christ child; in another window is a photograph of a lily faced little boy from Alan's class recently deceased, the photograph lined in black and decked among russet cigarette boxes; bicycle spokes shine and swerve; a newspaper headline wriggles under foot and wriggles out again.

On this street are women whose daughters married Protestants and went to America and lost their sons because of it; women whose sons have given their lives for Ireland, dying in the recent war of independence or civil war; women who are dying themselves; or women merely ferrying home groceries to country homes.

On this street are young men on bicycles; young men at corners; young men taking part in the Christmas pageant and mentally preparing for it; young men ruminating over a childhood history lesson, trying to put the pieces together again to make a whole; young men about to cycle home to country cottages and masturbate on kitchen hearths; young men imaginatively christening their first-born; young men who fought and were wounded; young men whose wounds festered and rendered them incapable of anything but standing on the main street and displaying their wounds, stumps of arms, of legs; young men still planning ambushes; young men thinking of nothing; young men about to go; young men who have stayed too long.

'Ah my dear. Ah my darling.' At the down-sloping and solely residential lower end of town Miss Kitty tries to seize Alan. Miss Kitty is so called because people have long forgotten her second name. But Alan eludes her black skirts beside her window in which her false teeth gape beside geraniums and she is left to wander up the street, arms still out, so swift is Alan's disappearance from under her.

The Shannon gleams now, in broad surface, in winter flood.

Lorcan stopped here once, further up, by Lough Ree, on his way up to Trinity College, on horseback; he descended from his horse and naked swam. At first he strode slowly into the water. Then he went more quickly, water enveloping his pale buttocks with red craters of a rash on them. His hands strove through the water. He was surrounded by awakening waterlilies and dozily drifting swans, the swans piquantly looking at him so gentle were his movements, he thought of the legend of the Children of Lir which his mother had told him in a stone floored room in Galway city, little men with plumes on their hats running in a courtyard in the fire, when he was a child; young people transformed into swans and destined to remain swans until Christianity touched the arteries of Ireland. But as swans hurled themselves into the air in sudden nervousness, an avenue of blinding light, he saw it differently; human flesh breaking into a flight of swans. 'Always trying, trying always to be different from what we are,

185

to metamorphose, to change our shape, to take flight, to forget, to be released, to be healed, to soar, to be anew. But some of us fail in flight. Some of us fall to the ground. And others – others go on through the trees until we hear the children, until we see the swing, until we reach for the child.' After his swim Lorcan dried himself, put on his clothes, sat and opened a Bible his tutor had given him. 'Consider the lilies of the field, how they grow; they toil not, neither do they spin: And yet I say unto you, that even Solomon in all his glory was not arrayed like one of these.' When Lorcan looked up there were few lilies to be seen, miles and miles of illuminated bog cotton though, dredges and furrows of bog cotton blowing across the Midland plain right to the low, distant Tipperary mountains. Lorcan closed his book with a thump, jumped on his horse and rode on towards Dublin, a trail of cloud in the blue sky which could have been the marking of a fighter bomber going over.

Alan wobbles up a pathway now to a house on a swiver of the Shannon. The house was burned down during the civil war. It belonged to two Protestant ladies. The house having survived the war of independence when it should have been burned down; in the early summer of 1922 the two ladies took in a little boy left by the tinkers at the site of their former encampment on a laneway near the house. Why the tinkers should have left this little boy nobody could guess. Perhaps he'd chosen to be left. He never said. The tinkers had spent the previous winter grabbing chickens by the neck from the yard and refurbishing themselves with apples from the garden, but generally a calm had existed between the house and the tinker encampment with its lazy, curling smoke. The little boy had black hair striped over his forehead, cherry dapples on his cheeks, some teeth missing, wore a dark little jacket and did tap dances for them in the hall when the door was open to the summer evening. He paid for his upkeep by doing little errands, fetching things, raking the garden, telling stories. He gasped out wild stories for the demure Protestant ladies of town. He stood and looked outwards as he told his stories and did not look at them, or their parasols, as if he was being visited by visions. Charlie the two Protestant ladies had called him. What his real name was no one knew, but that suited him. He played tennis with them, swooping at them on the lawn in front of the house on summer evenings, a parasol in one of their hands, tennis racquet in the other, fluff blowing through the air, an endless profusion of it, as if it were being released by a machine somewhere, the fluff becoming iridescent and the sound of their voices and the plopping ball dampened by dew. Neither of the ladies had ever been married and so neither ever had children of their own, and they dolled him up like a king, cap and stockings on him, and brought him on excursions in their boat up and down the Shannon, their parasols up, white dresses on them, he sat up, a hand perched on either side of the boat, his figure countering them. They were at pains to send him to Mass because they certainly would have offended the locals otherwise, but he still became known as 'the Protestant child'. The Protestant child continued to mesmerise them, telling stories in the hallway, standing, hands behind his back when the door was left open to the evening, his shirt collar now shining white against his dark jacket, the patterns of the floor emblazoned by sun. One of the ladies remarked how he always looked to the west, to the sea, on these occasions, as if that provided his inspiration. A road passed the gates to the house on which tinkers regularly, tranquilly travelled to the Atlantic. Towards the end of the summer, new mown grass in layers on the slope in front of the house, the harvest fields around telegraming their scents to the house, the ladies gave a hooley as they delicately referred to it. Protestant ladies eagerly spooned into gooseberry meringue as the little boy sang a song by the open doorway, a pale blue vest on him, short, wing-like trousers, boots, his hands behind his back, his face having become golden like the harvest fields, estuaries, streams of freckles running into it, his dark hair having lightened too, a stubble of red glints in it, his eyes looking in the direction of the west, incandesced. He bawled out the song. His voice became hoarse in the singing of it. The intricacies of patterns on the floor stood out in gold, hesitating to red. The song was about tinkers who departed to San Francisco and were duly lamented by their people while all the time they were careering around the streets of San Francisco with pint glasses of beer. Such was the little boy's concentration that he and the entire population of Protestant ladies of Athlone were wafted across the ocean to San Francisco where the ladies flustered about, unsure of what to do among the many smoky lettered windows of cocktail bars. A single blonde Edwardian girl stepped out of two Protestant ladies and walked across the harvest fields, sometimes a parasol over her, sometimes no parasol on her person, especially as she stopped to pluck pink roses on the edge of the harvest fields. As she approached, a brooch could be seen on her breast. On the brooch a young man, his black, Spanish hair merging into a pale, semitic face. A face that did not exist. A brooch that stated it was to be excellence or nothing and if nothing at least there was a moment of youth in a white, stem-like dress, among the harvest fields, when she was giving all of herself to an unknown young man. 'I tried to reach you. I tried to say hello. I wrote my book and I took my life because you were not there, you would not react. Why did you all hate me? Why did you all hate me so much?' (Beside Alan's obituary in the local newspaper was a photograph of a young man playing rugby in a blue and white striped jersey, stampeding towards the ball in obviously unsavoury weather in one of the first games of the season.) In the silence when the little boy waited for an echo from the sea, applause, or to remember another endless verse, his hair and his face one now like the harvest fields, the same silent pall on them, his hands still behind his back, an invisible camera popped, a photograph was taken and he was engraved among the more precocious presences of the house. Some of the ladies had come by boat and there were lanterns by a makeshift pier, boats shunting off in both directions, lanterns reflected on the waters, a cross-weaving of purposes, when the little boy disappeared. He did not take any silver or jewels as the more prescient supposed he would – nor did he take their father's bowl-like silver cup, won in a blue and white striped jersey in rugby championships in Dublin, as certain ladies especially predicted he would – but he made off as mysteriously as he came, a refrain of his song still stumbling across the harvest fields. Whether he took the road west or not no one knew, but he left a hush in the two ladies' lives, an unease. He'd warded off misfortune and now he left them open to all kinds of misfortune. Umbrellas over their heads, even when it was not raining, they scurried down, past the wet mown grass, to drop letters in the mail-box, hesitantly looking around at first. The red apples of autumn sploshed into the long untidy grass under the orchard trees. They kept to one room, big fires rumbling in the big dark room. In the spirit of the little boy they told one another ghost stories, but then remembered the only too real ghosts of the house – red coats in the end of the eighteenth century who'd made a foray from the house into the neighbouring county of Roscommon and massacred a peasant family there, grandparents who'd offered no succour to the starving during the Famine – and stopped. Besides the little boy seemed the real ghost of the house. They glided pots of soup onto the fire in the room where they slept as well as conversed. A man belatedly came to paint the red mail-box green. Then one night they thought they heard the little boy singing. His voice rasped out. His ghost filled the house. But the voice belonged to Malachy Heffernan whose brother had recently been killed by the Free Staters in the civil war, taken out in his pajamas, tied to a post beside barbed wire in the bog, blindfolded and shot. A blazing torch in his hand he called up to the two ladies, who were now standing terrified at their window, that they were Protestant biddies and loudly remonstrating with them that

188

it had been because of centuries of unbudging British rule that Irishmen were killing Irishmen now. He then proceeded to push the torch through the drawing-room window, the jaded carpet quickly took flame. The two ladies scampered out in their cotton night-dresses, one of them, the taller one, still ridiculously clinging to a hot water jar. They turned with the rest of the silent, growing pool of spectators, beside a swing by which they'd taken turns pushing the little boy in summer, and watched, sparks on the river – a host of carnival, lighted boats dizzying around on a lake in India during a British officers' party – as if they were mere onlookers to a village circus, a little girl now tugging one of their nightdresses, the consuming of their tall and gracious ancestral home against the black, starlit night.

Lessons swirl in Alan's mind, many lessons, history lessons, catechism lessons, but now that it is coming towards Christmas one lesson more than any other dominates, that of the three wise men. For weeks they have been coming, they have been travelling, they have encountered many dangers, much opposition on the laps of their journey. Slaughter was put in their way. Huge, gruesome, green, pink spotted snakes writhed in their path. Kings ordered their annihilation and witches threw spells, adverse to them, into cauldrons, their eyes all the time on them in crystal balls. But with the guidance they prevailed. They came safely through the desert and took a dinghy across the sea. They have now stepped onto a green land. They are on solid earth again. Many times Alan attempted his poem but the time was not yet right and he put down his pen, first dropping spare beads of ink into the inkwell as a teacher's voice trailed into the only tableau showing non-Irish soil on the wall, the site of the Battle of Banbury 1649 when young Englishmen tried to stop other young Englishmen from going to and marauding Ireland. In the picture the bodies of those who tried to stop the others lie in fields, on hills, in trees, under scarecrows, on ladders, under horses, by wagons, they threaten to fill the sky as well as the green, overburdened land; a young man is slumped on a mule. The worst atrocity is committed by brother against brother the teacher often whispers to an uncomprehending class. Especially by brothers who once shared in, who caroused and laughed over the same idealism. To see in others what you once had is a terrible fate, the teacher mumbles, and leads to murder. The splashes of poppies and blood in the picture are ample evidence of the truth of his remarks.

The two ladies did not leave. They moved into a little lodge house, long abandoned, by a stream running from the Shannon. Tinkers passed right beside them now, often red scarves around their necks, reins shivering in their hands. The locals even spoke of courage, identifying with them in their misfortune, one woman vociferously arguing they were human. The two ladies had a nephew in Dublin who visited them once or twice to help them make bilberry wine. He was tall, had red hair, streaks of gold in his red hair, wore white, attended Trinity, that ultimate fortress of perfidy and iniquity, was known to cycle a penny-farthing bicycle around town, one hand on the handlebar, the other sweeping back a streak of gold or amber hair. When Alan was four he was walking by the Shannon one afternoon. It was a sunny summer's afternoon. He encountered the young Protestant. The young man took Alan's hand, wordlessly at first, and led him by the Shannon. There were yellow irises by their feet and on the opposite bank, under tentative cypresses, cows, unusually pale for this part of Ireland. The young man began to tell Alan the story of Joseph and the dream Joseph interpreted for Pharaoh, seven fat cows for the good years. In his shrill Protestant voice, gold beads assembled in his eyelashes, the young man asserted the good years were coming. In his white, newly laundered shirt, sticking to the pink of his ribs, in white, immaculate trousers which glided along as his head bobbed, up and down, he went on to the story of Benjamin and Joseph, Benjamin being the youngest brother, the only one of his brothers who did not hate Joseph and desire him murdered. There were some brothers whose brotherhood remained intact, the young man said. Some brothers whose brotherhood survived in spite of everything. Such were they, he and Alan, on that fine summer's day when the tricolour at long last fluttered over the G.P.O. in Dublin, green and gold with white between, Wolfe Tone's dream, but the white already murky, the flag already weary and resigned in its batting, the Union Jack still stolidly singing against the elements over Stormont Castle in the orange demesne of Ireland. The young man did not say very much more, just leading Alan, who was making eddying efforts to keep up, on, his pale freckled hand tightening on Alan's hand, until he made some passing comment on the green, solvent land rising to greet them over the horizon.

The three wise men approach the Christ child now but this is a nativity scene unlike any other, it is an illustration from a book of seventeenth-century Irish history; to the right-hand side of the picture shepherds, in wolfskins, stand, the top part of them disproportionate to the rest of them, balloon-like, lambs in their arms, a craning gander in one person's arms, flourishing moustaches and beards hiding their features all but the milky wonder in their eyes, breeches laced up, their postures unbalanced – the draughtsman was drunk. Mary wears a black dress, its edges lined with glass beads, a white mantle on her head, a black wooden cross on the pale skin below her neck, her face demure and inclined like that of most women in books of Irish history, women who have been silently waiting for so long. Now the waiting has paid off. Kneeling, Mary looks gratified at the child. On the other side Saint Joseph is much like one of the shepherds. To the left side of the shed a man contorts with a music box. Above angels, emerald awnings all they're allowed for bodies, herald the birth, one bulbous fellow to the extreme left blows into bagpipes. The sky is phosphorescent with stars and yet each star is distinctive. In the distant rocky terrain through a window we see a fire blaze in a castle. The three wise men approach by way of a brook. Out of season furze and a bush of holly blossom beside the brook. One of the wise men – the fat one – bears honey. Wolfhounds, cattle, donkeys congregate around the child, one cow with particularly heavy breath, a tunnel of breath issuing from him. A robin is sentry above, a bead from his red breast dropping. But it is the child that breaks the spell of the picture, of the tapering, fossilized Mary, of the frozen shepherds; in his prison of linen bandages he beams with laughter and under the influence of the big star his hands outstretch, welcoming the gifts and the stares of onlookers, his cheeks red and round as polished apples in a Protestant ladies' garden.

Eventually the two ladies' faces sank in and they left. Alan watched from across the Shannon, poppies at his laceless boots, hands behind his back, a curl of his hair over his forehead a nun at school had christened 'marauder', as their piano was borne away, gagged, on a horse-drawn barrow; the movements of the piano, the rhythms of the horse, the trundling of the barrow registered in his dark, motionless eyes. Rearing over the other side of the Shannon, into the afternoon haze, all the way down along were white façades, other than that of the sisters, far larger than that of the sisters, the inkling of summer on them and loaded greenhouses and bracken pale orchards pressing alongside them. Somehow the piano ended up in England because one of the sisters wrote to a local Catholic woman who had befriended her in the latter days and said she now played the piano in a red brick cottage in the back streets of Birmingham, a piano thumping out from a red brick cottage among a myriad other red brick cottages in the splashing winter sunsets.

The winter sun is going down now over the Shannon and is reflected on an upper, cracked window. It is as if the two ladies are looking out, their lips gaunt as November carnations, their heads close together, fearful of what the night will bring, fearful of what life will bring, fearful of what this land will bring and is commonly known for – the untoward assassin, whether of the emotions or the body, the intruder in the night, the gun in the bushes, the rupturing insult that will destroy for life – but sure of this, the discordant rhapsodies of the heart.

The dead of the Battle of Banbury will litter the mind for ever and the dead of Drogheda and Wexford and New Ross. There will be new dead, other carnages. The contumely of brother against brother, the sidelong hatred, the muffled sound of spite will stick in the head. (I wish I could stop all this but hatred will not yield; I wish I could brush it away, the power of spite, the remembered slights, a kind of lingering gunpowder.) There are those among our ancestors who will haunt the mind too, a woman in a brown suit by a station, her brown hair in a heavy bun at the back, a pale blue brooch with a white mother and child on it on her jacket lapel, white lace at her neck, a hesitance about her poised right foot, purple lilac committing suicide on rusted railings behind her and in the whites of her eyes the breadth of visions, the beginnings of worlds that can only end in tears, in the upshootings of red in those whites, in the knowledge of death, a glass dome over plastic flowers in a graveyard in the low, hilly eastern Midlands, reflecting and ensnaring all who venture near. There are adolescents who will for ever stand under trees, a boy in blue denim, a girl with black hair, a troubled red-haired young man, discussing the apocalypse of the world and the unlikelihood of man's survival. A young man's face takes form out of the fluttering of the green, white and gold. But it is not an anticipated face. It is that of a young man in a white shirt, in a collegiate of places, walking sidelong against a brilliant blue sky on a beach in California, raising a rucksack onto his back again in the village of Delphi, his back to the white semi-fallen columns and a stripe of white birds that happens to be transfixed in flight across the columns as he sets off, the young man's face, no matter where he is, showing the inset of a struggle to be free of nation. A British soldier stays up into the night, writing a book which returns him to a childhood he never had and which repaints the walls of stale graffiti for him with ice maidens and with many necked, white, melting palaces. But now there is something else that was not there before. The world of Alan Mulvanney splayed into the poppies beside the Shannon last September – his body was found beside the Shannon – leaps to attention again, the lavishly black-haired Hollywood ladies in long strawberry coats, the more sedate women in brown suits and white silk blouses. The king of the fair is crossing a part of the Green which is blond rather than green, a gold tinsel sceptre in his right hand, the fat, red faced man chanting a rhyme chanted for centuries on these occasions. The mantra goes back further than history and reaches the ears of and revives a part of the memory lying on the ocean bed. On the dark solemn green again two armies in scarlet coats stand back, about to confront one another, sprays of poppies about to be trodden upon and kicked underfoot. A soldier in more modern uniform stands outside a cinema in Oxford for some reason, his bags beside him, waiting for a truck to pick him up, on the first stage of a return trip to Ireland, the portrait of Red Hugh O'Donnell suddenly appearing on the cinema poster behind him. A bouquet of flowers is raised to the sun, light penetrates its reds and its purples and its pinks and its yellows and its blues and its whites and its greys. Something of its radiance falls on the little boy at the desk about to lift his pen and write a poem. One moment the battle is at a pitch, the next the soldiers still moving towards one another, spears slanted in front of them, the wood enmeshed. And in this rotation further magic takes place. The two armies become many platoons, fragments, rectangles of opposing armies, scarlet banners tapering into an unsuspected breeze, white horses with their heads bowed self-satisfiedly, the glint of spear-heads like beds of new forest, each fragment in ratio to another fragment in the hills, in the fields, an effulgence on the point of battle. A hullabaloo ultimately rises into the sky from this battle as from the conflux of a hurling match. The babbled misgivings of adolescents under trees about the survival of the world become more intense. A little boy, beside his mother, in Dublin, under Nelson's Pillar, flowers, mainly yellow, bursting in their brown boxes beside flower-sellers, looks to where a splash of still fresh blood, shed in the recent civil war, is being pointed to on the clean pavement. But the screams subside into peonies on the library window. They are hushed as a woman in a brown suit, an Irish woman, head bent, crosses a field in Cambridge looking down at the bluebells at her feet. They are eclipsed by the rising articulation of a fairy story by a little boy, taking over even the idiotic chanting of a rhyme by the king of the fair and the sonorous garbling of a prayer by a young man, in an unmistakeable Athlone accent. 'Far, far from the land, where the waters are . . .' A child who was lost, feared drowned, missing, has been found, has come together again. He is panting up a path by the Shannon, the bric-à-brac of past and future lives in his head and among the trepidations of jackdaws on looming, bony, phosphorescent trees, the fluctuating mutterings of voices from another age, to a house where two Protestant ladies once lived.

Alan does not know why he has come here. He always comes here when something momentous has happened in his life. He's been bursting to come since he wrote his poem. It is his place, his ruin. To its devastation he brings his poem.

Alan turns now and, as he does, beside the pale blue, scorched door, under winter blossom, our eyes meet and something miraculous happens, the little black curly-haired boy in the short blue coat, poem in his hand, a smile on his lips because he knows something has happened today which will not stop today but which will go on, however little he understands it, becomes another little boy, a little boy who has been coming together, piece by piece, for a long time now, the bushel of copper hair over his forehead, the freckles under his eyes, his blue and white striped T-shirt. He was a talisman on nights in a mental hospital corridor, nights of orange lights, of the Sacred Heart picture and the assassin's bullet. He accompanied me through the desert, over the sea, through these pages. He kept me going when there seemed to be nothing else. Hands behind his back he occupies the sky now. But something seems to have happened to the world around him – has it been destroyed? But the little boy is smiling. He is smiling because he is remembering a snowman his father once told him about, a bowler hat on the snowman's head, spectacles on his nose, a black umbrella by his side, the snowman rising now over the glassy, blue, winter horizon – like a cloud.

Iowa City October 1981 – Heptonstall, Yorkshire March 1983.